The ADHD Parenting Solution

9 Proven Strategies For Behavior Management, Coping Techniques, Navigating Family Dynamics, and Building Emotional Support

HopeHarbour Publications

Dedicated to all the Neurodivergent individuals on Earth; you are miracles to a world that wasn't ready for your greatness.

People with ADHD often have a special feel for life, a way of seeing right into the heart of matters, while others have to reason their way methodically.

– Edward M. Hallowell

Contents

Introduction

I n the heart of every household, there lies a challenge that often goes unseen but is acutely felt. It's a challenge that doesn't discriminate based on age or background, affecting millions of families across the United States and the world. Did you know that in 2023, a staggering 265,000 children aged 3-5, 2.5 million kids aged 6-11, and 3.3 million kids aged 12-17 have ADHD? This isn't just a statistic; it's a reality that countless parents face daily (Wirth, 2023).

Imagine the whirlwind of emotions that parents grapple with as they navigate the unpredictable path of raising children with ADHD. The battles with homework, the worry about social acceptance, and the exhaustion from feeling like you're constantly walking a tightrope. These challenges are real, but there's hope, and it begins with understanding.

What prompted you to pick up this book? Was it a call from your child's teacher, a moment of desperation when you realized traditional parenting strategies weren't working, or a profound desire to provide the best possible life for your child? Whatever it was, this book was created with you in mind.

As a parent who has walked in your shoes, I understand your pain deeply. I've experienced the frustration of managing behaviors, the heartache of watching my child struggle, and the exhaustion that comes with the territory. I get it.

As you delve deeper into the chapters, you'll come to realize that the journey of parenting a child with ADHD is not only about managing their symptoms; it's also about understanding and embracing their unique strengths and talents. You'll learn to tap into your child's incredible potential and help them shine in ways you never thought possible.

The ADHD Parenting Solution is more than a book; it's a lifeline to a brighter future for your family. Let's explore what lies within its pages through the *BEATITUDE* solution:

- **B**roaden Your Knowledge: We'll begin by broadening your understanding of ADHD and how to support your child effectively. We will unravel the mysteries of ADHD, helping you see the world through your child's eyes. It's the foundation upon which everything else is built.
- **E**mpower Yourself: Recognize that empowerment starts with you. Learn to navigate the unique challenges that arise if parents have ADHD themselves, transforming potential burdens into strengths. Life will inevitably throw challenges your way. Discover how to nurture your child's resilience, equipping them with the tools to overcome adversity.
- **A**sk the Right Questions: Discover how to ask the right questions about treatment for ADHD and comorbidities, ensuring your child receives the best care possible. Learn the importance of self-care and

practical ways to recharge, ensuring you can be the best parent possible.

- **T**alk and Bond with Your Child: Effective communication is critical. You'll find guidance on conversing with your neurodivergent child without yelling or becoming overwhelmed by emotions. Every child needs emotional support, but it's especially vital for those with ADHD. Learn how to provide effective support to help your child thrive emotionally.

- **I**nstitute Structure: Implementing structure at home can be transformative. Step-by-step instructions will help you create an environment that welcomes peace and adaptability. ADHD doesn't stop at the school gates. Find techniques to manage your child's behavior in various settings, ensuring they can navigate the world successfully.

- **T**ransform Into an Advocate: Become your child's most ardent educational advocate. Empower them to thrive academically by understanding their unique needs. Uncovering the secrets to help your child excel academically is an essential step toward success in education.

- **U**nderstand and Reshape Behavior: Discover unique positive reinforcement strategies to manage behavior and foster a more harmonious family life. Behavior management in parenting a child with ADHD requires a unique approach to discipline that preserves their self-esteem while maintaining order.

- **D**esign a New Family Dynamic: Create a family dynamic that allows everyone to thrive together. Find ways that each member can contribute positively.

Your family is a team, and each member plays a crucial role in supporting your child.

- **E**xplore the Future: Look ahead to anticipate how your neurodivergent child will change as they age and learn how to prepare for the challenges and opportunities. Celebrate the success stories and envision a brighter future for your family; this is the culmination of your journey, where you see the tangible result of your efforts.

What sets this book apart is its unique approach, encapsulated in the *BEATITUDE* solution, designed to guide you through nine strategies for helping your child with ADHD thrive while ensuring everyone in the home flourishes. These steps are not theoretical; they come with techniques and practical tools to assist you every step of the way.

Picture a parent who once felt isolated and overwhelmed, not confidently guiding their child through the ups and downs of ADHD with compassion and grace. Imagine the joy of watching your child make friends, excel in school, and develop a strong sense of self-worth. These outcomes await you on this journey—those of resilience, determination, and unwavering love.

The result you can expect from reading this guide is nothing short of transformational. There is a family where homework time is no longer a battle, meltdowns are a rarity, and your child thrives academically, socially, and emotionally.

I'm a parent who has been where you are. I have successfully raised a 20-year-old son with ADHD, navigating the challenging waters of bipolar depression and anxiety. Every twist and turn in my parenting journey has been a learning experience, and I've dedicated two decades to understanding ADHD inside and out.

The journey took a lot of work. There were moments when I felt overwhelmed and uncertain, but I refused to give up. Raising a child with ADHD isn't a solo act; it's a family effort. Every member, from siblings to my partner, played a crucial role in our child's success. Through sheer determination and relentless education, I found ways to help my child at school and during extracurricular activities, significantly improving our entire family's journey and happiness.

While there can be occasional challenges, they no longer feel like insurmountable mountains because everyone is prepared for them. I traveled this path while unknowingly having ADHD myself. My diagnosis escaped detection until my mid-30s. That diagnosis has allowed ADHD to become a welcome part of my family while striving to help other families dealing with the condition succeed in all areas of life.

As you hold this book, know you're not alone in this journey. The solutions you seek are within reach. This is your guide to a brighter future, where ADHD doesn't define your child; it's just one aspect of their extraordinary potential.

As you embark on this empowering journey, you'll find the support, understanding, and strategies to create a thriving and harmonious family dynamic.

This is the right book for you, and it's time to take that first step toward a brighter tomorrow. Welcome to the world where challenges become stepping stones to success and your family's love and resilience shine brighter than ever before.

Chapter 1
Broaden Your Knowledge to Help Your Child With ADHD

I n the mosaic of childhood, ADHD is a unique piece that adds complexity and vibrancy. It's essential to begin your journey through ADHD with a solid foundation of understanding. This chapter serves as your gateway to knowledge, illuminating the path to helping your child thrive within the embrace of your loving family. In this chapter, we explore ADHD by taking the crucial first step in the *BEATITUDE* solution, which involves profoundly understanding the condition.

ADHD, or attention-deficit/hyperactivity disorder, is not a solitary challenge. It often coexists with other aspects of your child's development, including mental health issues such as depression or anxiety. This chapter explores the prevalence of ADHD, dispels stereotypes, delves into the neurological underpinnings, and examines how it progresses as your child grows. It also emphasizes the importance of professional diagnosis and introduces available treatment options. By broadening your knowledge of ADHD, you empower yourself to understand your child better and navigate this journey together, embracing the strengths and challenges that come with it.

What Is ADHD?

Attention-deficit/hyperactivity disorder (ADHD) is a multifaceted neurodevelopmental condition that profoundly impacts the lives of millions of children and adults. To fully grasp its significance, breaking down this condition's core aspects and exploring the various dimensions is essential.

ADHD, as defined by the Centers for Disease Control and Prevention (CDC), is a neurodevelopmental disorder characterized by difficulties with attention, hyperactivity, and impulsivity. It affects children and adults, though it is most commonly diagnosed in childhood. ADHD can persist into adulthood, leading to lifelong challenges for those affected.

There are three primary presentations or types of ADHD, each distinguished by the prominence of specific symptoms:

1. Inattentive ADHD (predominantly inattentive presentation): Individuals with this type find it challenging to organize tasks, complete assignments, pay attention to details, or follow instructions or conversations. They are often easily distracted and may need to remember the routine elements of their daily lives.

2. Hyperactive-impulsive ADHD (predominantly hyperactive-impulsive presentation): This type is characterized by constant restlessness and an inability to sit still. Individuals may frequently interrupt others and have difficulty waiting their turn. They often act

without thinking through the consequences of their
actions.

3. Combined ADHD (combined presentation): This
   presentation is the most common and involves a
   combination of inattentive and hyperactive-impulsive
   symptoms. Individuals with combined ADHD
   exhibit characteristics from both of the other two
   presentations.

It's important to note that not all individuals with ADHD will
experience the same symptoms or exhibit them in the same way
or continuously. ADHD is a highly individualized condition,
and the specific presentation can vary widely from person to
person. What works for one person with ADHD may not
necessarily work for another.

ADHD is not a transient challenge but a lifelong journey with
a brain that functions differently. It is essential to refrain from
labeling it as a disorder, disease, or illness, as these terms carry a
stigma that can negatively impact individuals with ADHD.
Instead, it's more accurate to view ADHD as a unique
neurodivergence. Those affected by ADHD often struggle to
control their behaviors and attention, making daily life more
challenging.

ADHD in Boys Versus Girls

ADHD doesn't discriminate based on gender, but there are
notable differences in how it manifests and is diagnosed in boys
and girls. Boys with ADHD display more overt hyperactivity
and impulsivity, often leading to earlier diagnoses. These traits
are most commonly associated with ADHD, so parents and
teachers are more likely to notice when these occur. Boys may

display their symptoms by constant fidgeting, an inability to sit still, or not being able to follow instructions.

In contrast, girls with ADHD often exhibit more internalizing symptoms, such as daydreaming and inattention. They can also appear unorganized or overly forgetful. Their hyperactivity is seen through talkativeness at times rather than restlessness. Although less noticeable, this is equally concerning. This leads to under-diagnosis or misdiagnosis, as their signs are less conspicuous and disruptive in most settings. The Centers for Disease Control and Prevention (CDC) notes that boys are three times more likely to be diagnosed with ADHD than girls (*What Is ADHD?* 2021).

This disparity in diagnosis often means that girls do not receive the support and intervention they need until later in life, if at all. Girls with ADHD are more likely to encounter depression, anxiety, and eating disorders, making their journeys uniquely complex.

Girls often face significant social challenges. Some struggle to form and maintain friendships due to impulsivity and emotional sensitivity. However, boys struggle with conduct issues, tics, and oppositional defiant disorder. While facing social struggles, boys display challenges, such as aggressive behavior or difficulty cooperating in group settings.

Early diagnosis and support can significantly impact a child's academic, social, and emotional development. When the subtle signs in girls go unseen, they can carry an unknown ADHD into adulthood, affecting their careers, relationships, and overall quality of life. Recognizing and addressing ADHD early, regardless of gender, allows for strategies that work with their unique ADHD presentation, promoting a thriving life. Armed with knowledge and empathy, you can champion your child, ensuring they are seen, understood, and supported in their unique ADHD journey.

Causes of ADHD

The exact cause of ADHD is a topic of ongoing research. It results from a complex interplay between genetic, environmental, and neurological factors. While the precise mechanisms are not fully understood, research by the CDC has indicated that genetics play a significant role. Children with a family history of ADHD are likelier to develop the condition (*What Is ADHD?* 2021).

Additionally, certain prenatal and early-life factors have been associated with an increased risk of ADHD. These included exposure to tobacco smoke during pregnancy, premature birth, low birth weight, and lead exposure. However, it's crucial to note that these factors alone do not cause ADHD; they contribute to a complex web of risk factors.

Understanding the multifaceted nature of ADHD is crucial to providing adequate support and interventions for individuals with this condition (*Understanding ADHD: Information for Parents,* 2019). It's a lifelong journey, and by dispelling myths, recognizing individuals' differences, and embracing the diversity of minds, we can create a more inclusive and empathetic world for those with ADHD.

Understanding the ADHD Brain: Embracing Neurodiversity

The human brain is a marvel of complexity, and when it comes to ADHD, this complexity takes on a unique form. To truly support and uplift individuals with ADHD, it's crucial to delve into the nuances of how their brains function without delving into technical jargon or extremes. This understanding paves the way for empathy and effective strategies for managing ADHD. According to research studies by the Cleveland Clinic (2022), we find in-depth explanations of neurodiversity.

Differences in Brain Structure, Function, and Chemistry

If you've ever wondered what sets the ADHD brain apart, it boils down to structure, function, and chemistry differences. These differences are not deficits but variations that make each neurodivergent individual unique. It's akin to comparing two different car models with distinct engines, capable of incredible feats but engineered in their own way. ADDA's study lays out the importance of understanding the structure, function, and chemistry of ADHD (*Understanding ADHD*, 2022).

One area of the brain that garners significant attention in ADHD is the frontal lobe. This region plays a vital role in executive functions such as decision-making, planning, and impulse control. In individuals with ADHD, there are differences in how the frontal lobe operates, potentially affecting their ability to regulate attention, stay organized, and control impulses. For example, a child with ADHD might struggle to complete a task, follow instructions, or maintain attention during a class, not because they choose to but because their frontal lobe operates differently.

It's important to emphasize that children with ADHD do not choose to lack attention or exhibit hyperactivity and impulsivity. These behaviors are rooted in the intricate workings of their neurodivergent brains. Understanding this fundamental difference is the first step in fostering empathy and adequate support.

The Reality of Brain Chemistry

Another aspect that sets the ADHD brain apart lies in its chemistry. Neurotransmitters, such as dopamine and norepinephrine, play a significant role in regulating attention, focus, and impulse control. In individuals with ADHD, there are variations in how these neurotransmitters function, affecting their ability to concentrate and regulate their behavior.

These brain chemistry differences are not within a person's control. They are intrinsic to the neurodivergent brain and contribute to the unique way it processes information and responds to stimuli. It's crucial to recognize that individuals with ADHD aren't intentionally disruptive or inattentive; their brain chemistry shapes their experiences and behaviors.

Neurodivergent Versus Neurotypical

Your child is neurodivergent, whereas individuals with seemingly "normal" brain functions are referred to as neurotypical. This distinction is not a value judgment but an acknowledgment of the wide variety of human neurological experiences.

It's crucial to remember that even among neurodivergent individuals, no two are exactly alike. The personalities, preferences, and behaviors of neurodivergent individuals can vary widely, even when they share the same underlying condition. This diversity is a testament to the human brain's intricacies and individuality's beauty.

The Power of the Term "Neurodivergent"

Why is it better to use "neurodivergent" when discussing conditions like ADHD? The term "neurodivergent" is inclusive and respectful. It acknowledges the inherent worth and potential of individuals with ADHD and other neurodivergent disorders. It doesn't pathologize differences but celebrates them.

Using this term encourages a shift in perspective, promoting acceptance and understanding. It reframes the conversation around ADHD from one of disorders to one of diversity, fostering an environment where neurodivergent individuals can thrive and contribute their unique gifts to the world.

Understanding how the ADHD brain works is not about delving into technicalities or extremes but embracing the concept of neurodiversity. It's about recognizing that your child's brain functions differently, and that's not a limitation; it's a unique facet of their identity. By understanding and embracing neurodiversity, we create a world where every individual, regardless of neurological differences, can shine and contribute to a brighter future.

Exploring the World of Neurodivergent Children with ADHD

Understanding ADHD children extends beyond recognizing differences in brain structure, function, and chemistry. It delves into a comprehensive appreciation of their unique challenges, struggles, and the often-overlooked strengths they bring to the world. Let's explore these facets, backed by scientific studies and evidence according to the CDC (*What Is ADHD?* 2021)

Sensory Processing and Overload

For some ADHD children, sensory processing and overload are significant concerns. Sensory overload occurs when a child's brain struggles to process and filter sensory information effectively. A study cited by *Medical News Today* highlights that individuals with ADHD may have heightened sensitivity to stimuli, leading to sensory-processing disorders. Imagine being in a noisy classroom with multiple ongoing conversations, flickering fluorescent lights, and various tactile sensations. For a child with ADHD, this environment can be overwhelming, making it challenging to focus and engage. Recognizing these sensory sensitivities and providing a supportive environment to mitigate sensory overload is crucial.

Emotional Processing Challenges

Another area where ADHD children often struggle is emotional processing. These children often struggle to regulate their emotions effectively. This can manifest as mood swings, impulsive reactions (screaming or yelling), or difficulty understanding their feelings, causing them to shut down or act out in various ways. Imagine a child who experiences intense emotions like frustration, excitement, embarrassment, and joy. For an ADHD child, these emotions may feel like a rollercoaster, and they might struggle to manage them appropriately. Understanding these emotional processing challenges can help parents and caregivers provide the necessary support and strategies to help their child navigate their feelings.

Communication and Social Interactions

Communication and social interactions can be everyday struggles for ADHD children. Research from The Brain Balance Centers highlights that children with ADHD may experience difficulties in aspects of communication such as conversation skills, social cues, and understanding nonverbal cues like body language. Imagine a child who has trouble maintaining eye contact during a conversation, frequently interrupts others, or struggles to grasp the subtleties of social interactions. These challenges can lead to misunderstandings and social isolation. Recognizing these difficulties can prompt interventions that enhance a child's social and communication skills.

Comorbidities: It's essential to recognize that ADHD often coexists with other conditions or comorbidities:

- Autism Spectrum Disorder (ASD): A complex condition that varies in severity. It affects how a person communicates, behaves, interacts with others, and learns. It is the most common disorder that occurs with ADHD. Conversely, there are a quarter of children with ADHD that have low levels of ASD.
- Tics: Characterized by sudden, repetitive movements or sounds, are a condition that can co-occur with ADHD. Research suggests a higher prevalence of tic disorders in children with ADHD.
- Depression, Bipolar Disorder, and Anxiety: Various mental health conditions can also affect ADHD children. These disorders range from issues regulating the highs and lows of moods to the ability to manage their emotions. Recognizing the presence of these comorbidities is vital for providing comprehensive mental health care.
- Oppositional Defiant Disorder and Disruptive Mood Dysregulation Disorder: This disorder sometimes overlaps with ADHD, complicating diagnosis and management. These conditions involve symptoms of defiance, aggression, and mood dysregulation.
- Dyslexia and Dyscalculia: Learning disorders are significantly more common in children with ADHD.

Understanding this connection can prompt early
interventions and support to address specific learning
challenges.

In essence, understanding neurodivergent ADHD children
involves acknowledging the multifaceted nature of their
experiences. It means recognizing their sensory sensitivities,
emotional-processing challenges, communication difficulties,
and the potential for comorbid conditions. By embracing this
comprehensive perspective, parents, caregivers, and educators
can provide tailored support that empowers their children to
thrive and realize their unique potential.

---

*"ADHD is not a choice or bad parenting. Kids with
ADHD work twice as hard as their peers every day but
receive more negative feedback from the world."*

– DRB

Unraveling the Myths: Separating Fact from Fiction

In the world of ADHD, myths abound, and these
misconceptions can compound the challenges faced by
individuals with ADHD and their families. To empower
parents and caregivers on this journey, it's crucial to unmask
some of the most common myths that perpetuate
misunderstanding and stigma.

Myth 1: People with ADHD Must Try Harder

One pervasive myth surrounding ADHD is that individuals with their condition simply need to put in more effort. This oversimplification fails to recognize the complex neurobiological factors at play. ADHD is not a matter of willpower; it's a neurodevelopmental disorder characterized by differences in brain structure and functions.

Studies and experts emphasize that individuals with ADHD often expend considerable mental energy to focus and complete tasks. The struggle lies in sustaining attention and impulse control, which can be challenging even with substantial effort. The misconception that trying harder will resolve ADHD only adds unnecessary stress and frustration.

Myth 2: Children With ADHD Can't Focus at All

Contrary to the belief that individuals with ADHD cannot focus, the reality is more nuanced. ADHD is characterized by difficulties in sustaining attention and regulating impulses. However, it does not mean that individuals with ADHD are incapable of focusing.

ADHD often involves "hyperfocus," a state where individuals become intensely absorbed in an activity that captivates their interest. They can focus exceptionally well in such instances. The challenge lies in directing this focus toward more stimulating and engaging tasks.

Myth 3: Only Boys Have ADHD

ADHD is not limited to any gender. While it's true that boys are more commonly diagnosed with ADHD, it's essential to recognize that girls can also have ADHD. The misconception that only boys have ADHD has led to under-diagnosis and delayed intervention.

As mentioned earlier, girls with ADHD may present different symptoms, internalizing their struggles and exhibiting fewer disruptive behaviors. These differences in presentation can make it challenging to identify ADHD in girls, but it's crucial to recognize that it affects both genders.

Myth 4: ADHD Is a Learning Disability or Illness

ADHD is often misconstrued as a learning disability or an illness. However, it is a neurodevelopmental disorder. Learning disabilities typically refer to specific difficulties in acquiring certain academic skills, whereas ADHD encompasses broader challenges in attention, impulsivity, and executive functioning.

Furthermore, ADHD is not an illness in the traditional sense; it's a neurobiological condition rooted in brain differences. Viewing ADHD as an illness can perpetuate stigma and misunderstandings.

Myth 5: Children Outgrow ADHD

The belief that children naturally outgrow ADHD is another common myth. While some children may see a reduction in symptoms as they enter adolescence and adulthood, many individuals continue to experience ADHD-related challenges into adulthood.

ADHD is often a lifelong condition that may evolve. As individuals with ADHD mature, they may develop coping strategies and better self-awareness, which can help them manage their symptoms more effectively. However, ADHD does not simply disappear with age.

Myth 6: ADHD Results from Bad Parenting

Attributing ADHD to parenting styles or caregiver behaviors is a harmful myth. Parenting can influence a child's environment and support but does not cause ADHD.

Research shows that ADHD has a vital genetic component, meaning it often runs in families. Blaming parents for their child's ADHD can lead to guilt and shame, hindering adequate support and understanding.

Albert Einstein once said, "If I had an hour to solve a problem, I'd spend 55 minutes thinking about the problem and 5 minutes thinking about the solutions." This perspective underscores the importance of thoroughly understanding the challenges before seeking solutions.

In the case of ADHD, disproving myths is an essential step in gaining that comprehensive understanding. These myths can perpetuate stigma, hinder accurate diagnosis, and lead to misconceptions about the nature of ADHD. By dispelling these myths, parents and caregivers can embark on the journey of supporting their ADHD children with a clearer perspective and a more empathetic approach.

Empowerment begins with knowledge, and understanding the realities of ADHD is the foundation upon which effective strategies and solutions can be built. It's not about trying harder; it's about comprehending the unique aspects of ADHD, recognizing its diverse presentations, and acknowledging that it is not a reflection of parenting but a neurobiological condition. Through this understanding, parents and caregivers can better advocate for their children, access appropriate resources, and create an environment that fosters growth and well-being.

Chapter 2
Empower Yourself Before You Empower Your Child

Parenthood is an incredible journey filled with love, joy, and countless memorable moments. Yet, when raising a child with ADHD, this journey often comes with unique and sometimes overwhelming challenges. It's crucial to recognize that you're not alone in feeling the weight of these challenges. According to the Centers for Disease Control, raising a child with ADHD can be five times more expensive than raising one without it, adding stress to your life (*Data and Statistics about ADHD,* 2022).

As parents, we often hesitate to openly acknowledge the strain we experience because we fear being judged or misunderstood. But let me tell you, it's perfectly okay to admit that life with an ADHD child can be challenging. It doesn't diminish your love for your child; it's a reality you're facing. This chapter is about empowering you, the parent, because helping others starts with helping yourself.

In the following pages, we'll explore coping mechanisms to manage the unique stressors of parenting an ADHD child. We'll delve into insightful truths that reveal the positive aspects of ADHD, celebrating the qualities that make your child unique. And for those of you who may have ADHD yourselves, we encourage you to navigate this shared journey with empathy, resilience, and good mental health practices. Let's embark on this empowering journey together because you'll be better equipped to support your child effectively by nurturing your well-being.

Empowering Yourself: The First Step Toward Nurturing Your Child's Well-Being

In the intricate web of parenting, where your child's well-being takes center stage, it's easy to forget that you are an integral part of the performance. As parents, we often prioritize our children's happiness and growth while neglecting our own. However, the first actionable step in the *BEATITUDE* solution is pivotal: to focus on and empower yourself. But why is this so essential? Now, we will explore the profound impact ADHD can have on you, your partner, and your family's overall well-being.

For some parents, the journey of raising a child with ADHD is deeply intertwined with their own experiences of ADHD. The statistics suggest that a significant number of parents may have ADHD themselves. In such cases, prioritizing your mental health becomes crucial and a shared endeavor between you and your child. Seek the care of a mental health professional (therapist, psychiatrist) if you suspect you may also have ADHD. Understanding and managing your ADHD can equip you with valuable insights and strategies to benefit you and your child.

The research underscores the extensive influence parenting a child with ADHD has on parental mental health and marital quality. The challenges posed by a child with ADHD can lead to feelings of powerlessness and moments of being overwhelmed. It's important to acknowledge that these feelings are not a sign of weakness but a natural response to parenting a child with ADHD. Seeking support and guidance is not a sign of failure; instead, it is a proactive step to prevent stress from becoming overwhelming.

Stress is a natural reaction that serves as a biological response to perceived threats. It can even be beneficial in small doses, motivating us to act. However, the chronic stress that often accompanies parenting a child with ADHD can have profound implications for your health, work, and relationships. It's essential to recognize that sustained stress can affect your physical and mental well-being, potentially leading to health issues and straining your relationships.

By understanding the impact of ADHD on you and your partner and recognizing the importance of self-empowerment, you can take proactive steps to enhance your mental health and overall quality of life. This section equips you with the tools, strategies, and insights you need to navigate parenting while ensuring your well-being remains a priority. Remember, you can't give your child everything positive and have them be mentally healthy if you don't have it yourself. Let's begin this journey of empowerment together, paving the way for a brighter future for both you and your child.

The First Step to Empower Yourself: Seek Social Support

In parenting a child with ADHD, one aspect shines exceptionally bright: the importance of social support. It isn't just a step; it's the cornerstone of empowering yourself and reducing the stress often accompanying this journey. As you handle the challenges of ADHD, finding your support network can be transformative, providing solace, empathy, and practical guidance when needed.

Why Does Social Support Matter?

Social support is not merely a luxury; it's a fundamental need for our well-being. It encompasses emotional support, where you can lean on friends and family for understanding and empathy. It includes instrumental support, such as tangible assistance with daily tasks or childcare. And it involves informational support, which can provide valuable knowledge and resources.

Research suggests that social support is a buffer against stress, reducing its adverse mental and physical health effects. It helps create a sense of attachment and belonging, reminding you that you're not alone. When you connect with others who share your experiences, it fosters a sense of camaraderie and understanding.

But there's more to it than just stress relief. Engaging in acts of altruism, or selfless acts of kindness and support toward others, can boost the release of positive hormones, such as oxytocin. This makes you feel good and enhances your overall sense of well-being. Altruistic acts can be as simple as offering a listening ear or sharing your experiences with someone who needs it. This reciprocal support system can strengthen the bonds within your social network.

Where to Find Support?

Now that we've established the importance of social support let's explore where and how you can find support other than family and friends already in your network. Fortunately, numerous avenues exist to connect with others who share your journey.

- ADDA Online Support Groups: The Attention Deficit Disorder Association (ADDA) offers online support groups specifically tailored for parents and adults with ADHD. These groups provide a safe and understanding space to share your experiences, seek advice, and connect with others who understand your unique challenges. ADDA's support groups are a valuable resource, accessible from the comfort of your home. In addition, the social media app Facebook has many groups like ADDA that support parents and help with any questions or struggles you may be having.

- MeetUp: This versatile platform connects people with shared interests and goals. By searching for "parents of children with ADHD" on MeetUp, you can discover local groups and events where you can meet other parents facing similar challenges. Meeting in person allows for a more intimate connection and the opportunity to build lasting friendships.

- CHADD ADHD Support Groups: Children and Adults with Attention-Deficit/Hyperactivity Disorder (CHADD) is a reputable organization for ADHD advocacy and support. They offer ADHD support groups that can provide invaluable insights, coping strategies, and a sense of community. CHADD's groups often meet in person and online, offering flexibility to suit your needs.

- Parental Training in Behavior Management: Consider enrolling in a parent training program focused on behavior management. These programs equip you with practical tools and strategies to navigate the challenges associated with ADHD.

While seeking mental health care for stress and emotions is essential, behavior management training can complement this by providing you with actionable techniques for effectively addressing your child's ADHD-related behaviors. These programs also have other parents who can help provide support while engaging in ways to empower yourself.

Seeking social support is crucial to empowering yourself and reducing the stress of parenting a child with ADHD. Recognize that you don't have to navigate this journey alone; communities and resources are available to provide the understanding, guidance, and empathy you need. By connecting with others who share your experiences and participating in acts of altruism, you'll bolster your well-being and contribute to the support and strength of yourself and your child. Together, we can face the challenges of ADHD with resilience, support, and unwavering love.

"I prefer to distinguish ADHD as attention abundance disorder. Everything is just so interesting, remarkably at the same time."

- *Frank Coppola*, movie director

Unleashing ADHD Superpowers

In your journey to empower yourself as a parent raising a child with ADHD, it's vital to recognize that ADHD isn't unfortunate news. It harbors remarkable potential and a set of unique superpowers that can be harnessed for personal and professional success. By understanding and embracing these positive aspects of ADHD, you can cultivate a more optimistic perspective, foster resilience, and enhance overall well-being.

ADHD Superheroes: Famous Individuals Who Triumphed

To illustrate the untapped potential within ADHD, let's take a look at some remarkable individuals who have not only coped with ADHD but have also thrived in their respective fields:

Michael Phelps

Michael Phelps, the legendary swimmer and one of the most decorated Olympians of all time, discovered the power of self-discipline through his journey with ADHD. Despite facing challenges, he channeled his boundless energy into a relentless pursuit of excellence, becoming an iconic and legendary athlete.

Howie Mandel:

The zany comedian and television personality Howie Mandel has embraced his ADHD as a unique asset. His spontaneous wit and creativity, often associated with ADHD, have contributed to his success in the entertainment industry. Rather than viewing it as a hindrance, Mandel has harnessed his ADHD traits to connect with audiences on a profound level.

Terry Bradshaw

Super Bowl champion and renowned sports commentator Terry Bradshaw openly discusses how ADHD posed academic challenges during his school years. However, he credits his ADHD-driven resilience for motivating him to excel in sports.

Bradshaw's journey showcases how the qualities often associated with ADHD, such as determination and adaptability, can lead to remarkable achievements.

Unlocking the Six ADHD Superpowers

How and why do these individuals find a positive light in ADHD? The answer lies in recognizing and harnessing the six superpowers that often accompany this neurodivergent condition:

1. Hyperfocus: ADHD individuals possess the ability to hyperfocus intensely on tasks that captivate their interest. This superpower enables them to delve deeply into their passions and excel in specific areas.
2. Creativity: The ADHD brain thrives on creativity, often generating innovative ideas and solutions. This imaginative prowess can be valuable in various fields, from the arts to entrepreneurship.
3. Abundant Energy: While excessive energy can sometimes be viewed as a drawback, it also means that ADHD individuals often possess boundless enthusiasm and vigor. This vitality can fuel their endeavors and drive them to persevere through challenges.
4. Spontaneity: ADHD individuals embrace spontaneity and thrive in situations that require adaptability. This quality can be a valuable asset in fast-paced, ever-changing environments.
5. Resilience: Many ADHD individuals have developed resilience in the face of adversity. They've learned to overcome obstacles, bounce back from setbacks, and continuously push forward.

6. Conversational Skills: ADHD individuals often excel in conversation, naturally engaging others and connecting personally. Their conversational prowess can create strong relationships and networking opportunities.

Embracing Your ADHD Superpowers

Understanding these superpowers isn't only about recognizing them in others; it's also about acknowledging them within yourself and your child. While not all children with ADHD exhibit these traits to the same degree, they are undoubtedly strengths rather than disadvantages.

By fostering an environment that encourages the development of these superpowers, you can help your child harness their full potential. Encourage their interests, provide opportunities for creative expression, and enthusiastically support their endeavors.

As a parent, you can tap into these superpowers in your own life. Embrace your creativity, resilience, and ability to hyperfocus when needed. Channel your abundant energy into positive pursuits, and leverage your conversational skills to build a strong support network.

Recognizing and celebrating the positive aspects of ADHD can be a transformative step on your journey to empowerment. By embracing the unique superpowers that often accompany ADHD in yourself and your child, you can enable a sense of optimism, resilience, and achievement. Remember that ADHD isn't a limitation; it's a source of incredible potential waiting to be unlocked.

Building Resilience Through Mindfulness

In the journey to empower yourself as a parent raising a child with ADHD, you've already begun a remarkable transformation. You've recognized the challenges, harnessed the support of others, and celebrated the unique strengths that come with ADHD. Now, it's time to explore the final step in your empowerment journey: adopting coping mechanisms and a new mindset rooted in mindfulness.

Understanding Mindfulness and Its Resilience-Building Power

Mindfulness is a practice that cultivates your awareness of the present moment, helping you engage with life more fully and intentionally. By learning to be mindful, you can build resilience, enhance your mental well-being, and develop valuable coping mechanisms to navigate the complexities of raising a child with ADHD.

Scientific research supports the profound impact of mindfulness on resilience. Resilience refers to our ability to bounce back from adversity and adapt to life's challenges. Studies have shown that mindfulness can strengthen our emotional stability, improve stress management, and enhance our overall psychological well-being.

One of the core principles of mindfulness is paying attention to the here and now. By staying present in the moment, you can break free from worries about the future or regrets from the past. This practice can be particularly valuable for parents dealing with the demands of raising an ADHD child.

The Four Rules of Mindfulness in Overwhelming Moments

Mindfulness offers practical guidelines for maintaining your focus and composure during overwhelming moments. These principles can be your guiding light when stress and frustration threaten to take over:

1. Pay Attention: Start by directing your attention to the present moment. Observe your thoughts, feelings, and sensations without judgment, but also become more aware of the space in the world around you, the beauty of nature, and the serenity of silence. Acknowledge these elements as they arise, fostering a deeper connection with the environment and the stillness of the moment.

2. Breathe: Deep, intentional breathing is a cornerstone of mindfulness. Take a few slow, deep breaths to center yourself in moments of stress. Focus on the sensation of your breath as it enters and leaves your body.

3. Accept: Embrace the reality of the moment, even if it's challenging. Acceptance doesn't mean resignation; it means acknowledging your circumstances without resistance. This can alleviate inner turmoil and remind us that no matter what is going on, life changes, things happen, and we will persevere because everything is temporary.

4. Let Go: Release the need to control or change everything. Understand that some things are beyond your control, and that's okay. Letting go of unnecessary burdens can free up mental and emotional space.

The Power of Meditation: A Daily Resilience-Building Practice

Meditation is a foundational component of mindfulness that can significantly contribute to your resilience. It involves setting aside time each day to sit in silence, focus on your breath, and observe your thoughts without attachment. Meditation offers a profound opportunity to cultivate inner calm, clarity, and resilience.

It's important to note that meditation is a personal practice, and it's perfectly okay if it doesn't resonate with you immediately. Like any skill, it may take time to develop. Be patient and explore meditation techniques to find what suits you best.

Beyond Meditation: Five Mindful Activities for Coping and Resilience

While meditation is a powerful mindfulness exercise, it's not the only way to cultivate resilience and cope with the challenges of parenting a child with ADHD. Here are five alternative mindful activities you can incorporate into your daily life:

1. Mindful Eating: This practice involves savoring each bite of food with full awareness. Slow down and engage your senses as you eat, paying attention to your meal's textures, flavors, and aromas.
2. Mindful Walking: Take leisurely walks, paying close attention to each step and the sensations in your body as you move. Walking mindfully can help clear your mind and reduce stress. Walking in nature can help with clearing the mind.
3. Mindful Intimacy: Mindful intimacy is about connecting with your partner on a deeper level during intimate moments. Focus on the sensory experiences, emotions, and sensations shared with your loved one.
4. Mindful Journaling: Set aside time for reflective journaling. Write about your thoughts, feelings, and

experiences without judgment. Journaling can provide insights and emotional release.

5. Mindful Breathing Exercises: In addition to meditation, you can practice specific breathing exercises designed to calm your nervous system and reduce stress. These exercises can be done anytime, anywhere.

Incorporating these mindfulness activities into your daily routine can fortify your resilience and equip you with effective coping mechanisms. Remember that mindfulness is a journey; its benefits accumulate gradually over time. By embracing this practice, you'll empower yourself with the tools to navigate raising a child with ADHD while nurturing your well-being.

Interactive Mindfulness Activities

In your journey to empowerment as a parent of a child with ADHD, engaging in mindfulness practices that enhance your resilience and serve as positive examples for your child is essential. These mindfulness activities are for your well-being and can inspire your family to imitate and benefit from the positive changes you'll experience.

Before you start, remember that mindfulness is a skill that develops gradually. Be patient with yourself and practice these activities regularly to experience their full benefits. Here are five interactive mindfulness exercises to get you started:

Activity 1: Body Scan Meditation (Approximately 10 Minutes)

Body scan meditation is a practice that involves systematically focusing your attention on different parts of your body. It helps you become more aware of physical sensations and promotes relaxation. Here's how to do it:

- Find a quiet, comfortable space to sit or lie down.
- Close your eyes and take a few deep breaths to center yourself.
- Start at your toes and gradually work your way up through your body, paying attention to any tension or discomfort.
- As you scan each body part, visualize releasing any tension or stress with each exhale.
- Spend extra time on areas where you notice tension, allowing them to relax.
- Finish the scan at the top of your head, feeling a sense of relaxation and peace throughout your body.

Activity 2: Mindful Walking (Approximately 10 Minutes)

Mindful walking is a simple yet effective practice that allows you to connect with your surroundings while reducing stress. You can practice it indoors or outdoors. Here's how:

- Find a quiet place to walk, free from distractions.
- Begin walking at a slow, comfortable pace.
- Pay attention to each step, the sensations in your feet, and the movement of your body.
- Notice the sounds, scents, and sights around you without judgment.
- If your mind starts to wander, gently bring your focus back to the act of walking.
- Continue this practice for about 10 minutes, allowing it to ground you in the present moment.

Activity 3: Gazing Meditation (Approximately 5 Minutes)

Gazing meditation is a simple yet powerful practice that enhances your ability to focus and be present. You can do it indoors or outdoors. Here's how:

- Find an object to gaze at, such as a candle flame, a piece of artwork, or a natural scene.
- Sit comfortably and take a few deep breaths to relax.
- Fix your gaze on the chosen object without blinking excessively.
- As you focus on the object, notice its details, colors, and textures.
- Allow your mind to become absorbed in the act of gazing, letting go of other distractions.
- Continue for approximately 5 minutes or until you feel a sense of tranquility.

Activity 4: Mindful Breathing (Approximately 5 Minutes)

Mindful breathing is a fundamental mindfulness practice that can help calm your mind and reduce stress. Here's how to do it:

- Find a quiet space and sit in a comfortable position.
- Close your eyes and take a few deep breaths to center yourself.
- Shift your attention to your breath, focusing on the sensation of each inhale and exhale.
- Be fully present with your breath, observing its natural rhythm.
- If your mind wanders, gently guide your focus back to your breath.
- Continue this practice for about 5 minutes, allowing it to bring a sense of calm and clarity.

Activity 5: The 5-4-3-2-1 Technique (Approximately 5 Minutes)

The 5-4-3-2-1 technique is a quick and effective mindfulness exercise for grounding yourself in the present moment, especially during moments of anxiety or stress. Here's how it works

- Acknowledge five things you can see around you.
- Identify four things you can touch or physically feel.
- Notice three things you can hear in your environment.
- Identify two things you can smell. These can be scents in your surroundings or from personal items.
- Finally, recognize one thing you can taste or enjoy tasting. Savor that taste for a moment.

These interactive mindfulness activities offer a practical way to incorporate mindfulness into your daily life, even with a busy schedule. Engaging in them for an extended time is an option to consider with you and the family. Regularly engaging in these exercises will enhance your resilience, reduce stress, and build a positive mindset, setting a powerful example for your child and family.

Remember the words of Albert Schweitzer: "Do something wonderful; people may imitate it." Your journey to empowerment is an inspiring path that can positively influence those around you, ultimately helping you make informed decisions about every aspect of your life.

Chapter 3
Ask the Right Questions

In the parenting journey, particularly when raising a child with ADHD, understanding the available treatment options can be comparable to discovering hidden treasures. Every parent's quest is driven by the desire to provide their child with the best possible support and care. As we delve into this chapter, you will be guided through the rich landscape of ADHD treatments, therapies, and holistic approaches.

Research confirms that 77% of children diagnosed with ADHD follow a treatment plan (Wirth, 2023). Further research confirms that among the percentage of children diagnosed with ADHD, approximately 47.6% receive cognitive behavioral therapy (ADHD Statistics: New ADD Facts and Research, 2006). These numbers reveal the complexity of the ADHD treatment overview. The journey toward effective ADHD management involves navigating various options, each with unique considerations.

We aim to shed light on these diverse treatment paths, helping you comprehensively understand the available choices. Recognizing that the information presented here is not a substitute for professional medical advice is crucial. Instead, it is a valuable resource to empower you with knowledge, enabling you to make informed decisions that align with your child's unique needs and your family's circumstances. So, let's continue this enlightening expedition, exploring the domain of ADHD treatment types and uncovering the potential solution that may bring clarity and relief to your journey.

Exploring ADHD Medications: Finding the Right Path

Navigating the world of ADHD treatment options can be a complex journey, like charting a course through uncharted waters. As we set sail on this exploration, one of the initial islands we encounter is medication, the cornerstone of ADHD management. It is essential to begin by understanding that ADHD medications, in their various forms, play a pivotal role in altering the brain's chemical balance, helping to alleviate symptoms and improve daily functioning.

ADHD medications can be likened to keys that unlock a child's potential by addressing core challenges like inattention, impulsivity, and hyperactivity. However, it is essential to acknowledge that finding the proper medication and dosages can be a process that requires patience, close monitoring, and collaboration with healthcare providers. According to research by the Cleveland Clinic (2022), we find the different types of medication that can be used, including the side effects.

The Stimulant Story: Unveiling Two Types

Stimulant medications have been a cornerstone of ADHD treatment for decades, and they come in two main varieties: immediate-release and extended-release. Immediate-release stimulants provide rapid relief but have a shorter duration of action, typically requiring multiple daily doses. On the other hand, extended-release stimulants offer more sustained coverage, often allowing for one daily administration. The choice between them depends on factors such as the child's individual needs and the healthcare provider's recommendations.

With stimulant medications, you may encounter a variety of names, both generic and brand, each with its unique duration of action. Common stimulant medications include methylphenidate-based drugs like Ritalin and Concerta and amphetamine-based options such as Adderall and Vyvanse. The selection of a particular stimulant depends on various factors, including the child's response and any side effects experienced. Some common stimulant medications are:

- Methylphenidate (immediate release and extended-release): Sold under various brand names like Ritalin and Concerta, methylphenidate is one of the most well-known stimulant medications for treating ADHD.
- Amphetamine (immediate release and extended-release): Medications such as Adderall and Dexedrine contain amphetamine, another widely prescribed stimulant for ADHD management.
- Dexmethylphenidate (immediate release and extended-release): Dexmethylphenidate-based drugs, including Focalin and Focalin XR, offer options for those who may not respond well to other stimulants.
- Lisdexamfetamine (extended-release): Lisdexamfetamine, marketed as Vyvanse, is an extended-release stimulant known for its long-lasting effects.

- Mixed Amphetamine Salts (immediate release and extended-release): Sold under the brand name Adderall, this medication combines various amphetamine salts.

While stimulant medication can provide significant symptom relief, it is essential to be aware of potential side effects that may necessitate changes in medication or dosage. Common side effects can include sleep disturbances, decreased appetite, and, in rare cases, cardiovascular issues. Monitoring your child's response and maintaining open communication with their healthcare provider is essential to ensure the best possible outcome.

Non-Stimulant Medications

In some cases, stimulant medications may not be suitable or effective for a child with ADHD. In such instances, non-stimulant medication may offer an alternative path. These medications function differently, often focusing on enhancing neurotransmitters other than dopamine or norepinephrine.

Non-stimulant medications can have a longer duration of action, sometimes lasting up to 24 hours, which can benefit children who require symptom control throughout the day. Standard non-stimulant options include:

- Atomoxetine (Strattera): Atomoxetine is a selective norepinephrine reuptake inhibitor (NRI) that can help manage ADHD symptoms. It can be beneficial as an adjunct treatment or an alternative to stimulants.
- Guanfacine (Intuniv) and Clonidine (Kapvay): These alpha-2 adrenergic agonists can assist in reducing

impulsivity and hyperactivity. They are sometimes used as adjunct treatments or as alternatives to stimulants.

- Bupropion (Wellbutrin): While primarily an antidepressant, bupropion may help manage ADHD symptoms, particularly in adults.

The decision to opt for non-stimulant medications is guided by factors like a child's responses to stimulants, the presence of specific medical conditions, or concerns about stimulant-related side effects. These medications may be particularly suitable for children who experience tics or have a history of substance abuse.

Antidepressants and Comorbidity

In some cases, children with ADHD may also contend with comorbid conditions such as anxiety or depression. This complex interplay of disorders may require antidepressants to address emotional and mood-related symptoms. While the Food and Drug Administration (FDA) has not specifically approved antidepressants for ADHD treatment, healthcare providers may prescribe them as part of a comprehensive management plan.

It is essential to approach the use of antidepressants in children with caution, as a healthcare professional should closely monitor their safety and effectiveness. Open and transparent communication with your child's healthcare provider is vital to ensure that treatment aligns with your child's specific needs and minimizes potential risks.

Administering Medications Safely

As a parent, the responsibility of administering medication safely falls on your shoulders. To ensure that your child receives the intended benefits while minimizing risks, consider the following tips:

- Give Medication Carefully: Follow the prescribed dosage instructions diligently and never adjust the dosage without consulting the healthcare provider. Use measuring devices designed for medication administration to prevent errors.
- Establish a Routine: Consistency is critical in medication management. Establish a daily medication administration routine, making it a part of your child's daily schedule.
- Maintain Communication: Keep lines of communication open with your child's healthcare provider. Discuss any concerns, side effects, or changes in your child's behavior promptly.
- Secure Medications: Store all medications out of reach of children, in a safe location, and follow any specific storage instructions provided with the prescription.

Understanding the diverse world of ADHD medication is the first step in equipping yourself with the knowledge needed to make informed decisions for your child's well-being. Remembering medication is just one facet of ADHD management; a holistic approach that includes therapies, behavioral interventions, and a supportive environment is equally vital. As we journey further, we will explore these complementary elements to provide you with a well-rounded perspective on ADHD treatment options.

Addressing Side Effects

As with any medication, ADHD treatments can have side effects, which may vary from person to person. Awareness of these potential side effects is crucial to ensure your child's well-being while on medication. Common side effects associated with stimulant medications include:

- Decreased Appetite: Stimulants can reduce appetite, potentially leading to weight loss or slower growth in children. Monitoring your child's growth and eating habits is essential.
- Sleep Disturbances: Some individuals may experience difficulty falling asleep or disrupted sleep patterns while taking stimulant medications.
- Increased Heart Rate and Blood Pressure: Stimulants can temporarily elevate heart rate and blood pressure, necessitating regular monitoring.
- Mood Changes: In some cases, stimulant medications may affect mood or lead to irritability.
- Tics: In rare instances, stimulant medications may exacerbate or trigger tics (sudden, repetitive, nonrhythmic movements or sounds).
- Gastrointestinal Issues: Stimulant medication can cause stomachaches, nausea, or other gastrointestinal discomforts.
- Headaches: Some individuals may experience headaches as a side effect of stimulant medications.
- Dizziness or Lightheadedness: In rare cases, stimulant medications may cause dizziness or lightheadedness.

Should your child experience significant side effects or adverse reactions to their medication, it is essential to communicate promptly with your healthcare provider. Adjustments to the medication dosage or a change in prescription may be necessary to address these issues.

Exploring ADHD Therapies

Research conducted by the Mayo Clinic provides valuable information in understanding ADHD and its management (Attention-Deficit/Hyperactivity Disorder (ADHD) in Children Diagnosis and Treatment, n.d.). You will discover that medication is just one piece of the puzzle in the approach to effective ADHD management. It often requires a multifaceted approach, and therapies are vital in this intricate process. This section will explore the various therapeutic options available to families dealing with ADHD and shed light on their potential benefits.

The Power of Combined Therapies

Before delving into specific therapies, one must grasp the significance of a multi-pronged approach to ADHD management. While individual treatments can yield positive outcomes, the best result often arises when a combination of methods is employed. Collaboration among teachers, parents, therapists, and physicians creates a supportive network that enhances the overall effectiveness of ADHD management.

Educating yourself about ADHD and the available services is an invaluable first step. Work closely with your child's teachers and provide them with reliable sources of information to support their efforts in the classroom. By starting an open line of communication, you can ensure a cohesive approach to addressing your child's needs.

- Medication: While not a therapy in the traditional sense, medication plays a significant role in ADHD management. Stimulant medications, like methylphenidate and amphetamine-based drugs, are commonly prescribed to improve attention and impulse control. Non-stimulant medications, such as atomoxetine and guanfacine, may be suitable alternatives, particularly when stimulants are ineffective or have undesirable side effects.
- Social Skills Training: Social skills training helps individuals with ADHD improve their interactions and relationships with peers and adults. It focuses on developing communication skills, understanding social cues, and enhancing self-esteem, improving their ability to navigate social situations successfully.
- Parenting Skills Training: Parenting skills training provides caregivers with strategies and techniques to effectively manage the behaviors and challenges associated with ADHD in their children. It emphasizes consistent discipline, positive reinforcement, and a supportive home environment.
- Psychotherapy: Psychotherapy, including individual and group therapy, can benefit individuals with ADHD, especially when addressing the emotional and psychological aspects of the condition. It provides a safe space to explore feelings, develop coping strategies, and work on improving self-esteem.
- Behavioral Therapy: Behavioral therapy is one of the most commonly utilized therapeutic interventions for ADHD. This approach targets specific behaviors and aims to improve daily functioning, making it particularly beneficial for children with ADHD. Behavioral therapy equips

parents and children with valuable strategies to navigate the challenges associated with the condition.

- Combined Therapies: The most effective results emerge when combining multiple therapies. This approach involves collaboration among parents, therapists, and healthcare providers. By combining strategies from different treatments, individuals with ADHD can benefit from a comprehensive and personalized approach to management.

One essential aspect to note is that behavioral therapy often involves parent training. Parents play a crucial role in implementing behavioral strategies, making it necessary for them to receive guidance and support. This training empowers parents to effectively manage their child's behavior, reinforce positive actions, and provide constructive feedback.

Combining behavioral therapy with medication is a prevalent choice among parents and healthcare providers. For some children, especially those with severe ADHD symptoms, the synergy between behavioral therapy and medication can yield remarkable results. However, it is essential to remember that every child is unique, and the best approach will vary.

Cognitive Behavioral Therapy (CBT)

Cognitive Behavioral Therapy (CBT) is a form of psychotherapy focusing on cognitive and behavioral patterns. While it is not the primary treatment for ADHD, CBT can be instrumental when ADHD co-occurs with other conditions, such as depression or anxiety.

CBT benefits teenagers who may have developed better symptom-management skills but need support in improving essential life skills. It can aid individuals of any age in socializing, effective communication, and emotional regulation.

CBT's effectiveness in managing ADHD comorbidities underscores the importance of a thorough assessment and diagnosis. Identifying and addressing additional conditions is critical in providing comprehensive care.

Family Therapy

The final therapy on our list is family therapy, which benefits not only the ADHD child but the entire family unit. ADHD can impact family dynamics and relationships, requiring specialized intervention to help family members cope and thrive. Family therapy serves two primary purposes:

- Coping with ADHD: Family therapy equips parents and siblings with strategies to navigate the challenges posed by living with a child with ADHD. It fosters understanding and provides a safe space for open communication.
- Skill Development: ADHD can impact various life skills, such as effective communication, conflict resolution, and emotional regulation. Family therapy can help family members, including the ADHD child, improve these essential skills.

By engaging in family therapy, you create a supportive environment that strengthens your family's ability to manage the complexities of ADHD together. It can be a source of resilience, providing cooperation and empathy among family members.

A Holistic Approach to ADHD Management

In navigating the world of ADHD therapies, it is essential to recognize that there is no single solution. As a parent, you play a pivotal role in this journey. Collaborate with healthcare professionals, educators, and therapists to determine the most suitable therapeutic interventions for your child. Combining behavioral therapy with medication or CBT for comorbidities can yield positive outcomes. The key to success lies in understanding your child's strengths and challenges and addressing their individual needs. With a holistic approach to ADHD management, you can provide the support and tools necessary for your child to thrive.

Exploring Alternative Measures in ADHD Management

While conventional treatments and therapies are crucial in managing ADHD, some individuals and families seek alternative measures to complement their approach. It is essential to note that these alternative measures vary in terms of scientific support and may only work for some. Here, we briefly explore various alternative measures for ADHD:

- The ADHD Diet: Diet plays a significant role in overall health, and some families choose to explore dietary changes to manage ADHD symptoms. While there is no one-size-fits-all ADHD diet, some principles suggest that consuming whole grains, fruits, and fiber-rich foods can promote better brain health and potentially help with symptom management.
- The Feingold Diet: This Diet is a specific dietary approach that eliminates artificial colors, flavors, and certain food additives. Some parents have reported improvements in their children's behavior when

following this diet. However, it remains a subject of debate, with some experts questioning its effectiveness.

- ADHD Supplements: Various dietary supplements are marketed as natural remedies for ADHD. These supplements often contain omega-3 fatty acids, zinc, and magnesium. While some individuals report benefits, scientific evidence supporting their efficacy remains limited.

- Game-Based Digital Therapeutic Devices: Advances in technology have led to the development of digital therapeutic devices and apps designed to help individuals with ADHD improve their attention and focus. These games and tools may serve as complementary resources for managing symptoms.

- Meditation and Mindfulness for ADHD: Mindfulness practices and meditation techniques can aid individuals with ADHD in improving focus, impulse control, and emotional regulation. These practices encourage self-awareness and may provide valuable coping mechanisms.

- Chiropractic Care: Some families explore chiropractic care to address ADHD symptoms. Chiropractors believe that spinal adjustments can influence the nervous system and overall well-being. However, scientific evidence supporting chiropractic care for ADHD management is limited.

- Neurofeedback Training: Neurofeedback training is a non-invasive method that aims to improve self-regulation of brain function. It teaches individuals to modify their brain activity consciously. While some studies suggest potential benefits, more research is needed to establish its effectiveness.

- Melatonin: Melatonin is a hormone that regulates sleep-wake cycles. Some parents consider melatonin supplements to improve sleep patterns in children with ADHD, as sleep difficulties are common. However, consulting a healthcare professional before using melatonin supplements is essential.

Scientific research on the effectiveness of these alternative measures varies, with some showing promise while others require further investigation. Individuals and families must approach alternative measures with an open mind while maintaining realistic expectations. Alternative therapies are also available for pediatric attention deficit hyperactivity disorder (Searight et al., 2012).

Free resources are available to support parents and families in their ADHD management journey. These resources often include printable materials and guides with daily life tips, strategies, and reminders. They can be valuable tools for effectively implementing alternative measures and complementing conventional treatments. As you explore these alternative measures, remember that what works best will vary from person to person. Consulting with healthcare professionals, including pediatricians, psychologists, and nutritionists, can help you make informed decisions tailored to your child's unique needs and circumstances.

Unlocking Valuable Resources for ADHD Management

In your journey to support your child with ADHD, access to valuable resources can make a significant difference. These resources offer guidance, insights, and actionable strategies to help your family navigate the challenges of ADHD effectively. Let us explore some of these free resources available online, designed to empower parents and families:

ADHD-Friendly Eating Guide

ADDitude provides valuable resources on what foods to eat to improve ADHD symptoms. You can download a helpful brochure, Free Guide: What to Eat (and Avoid) for Improved ADHD Symptoms, at additudemag.com (Amen, D., & Amen, T., 2019).

Understanding the impact of nutrition on ADHD symptoms is essential. This resource provides insights into what to include in your child's diet for improved symptom management. It highlights food that can positively influence attention and focus while suggesting items to avoid. By downloading and printing this guide, you'll have a tangible reference to help shape your child's eating habits.

ADHD-Friendly Cooking Tips and Recipes

ADDitude also provides ADHD-friendly cooking tips and recipes to assist you in nutrition planning for your ADHD child (Free Guide to Delicious (and ADHD-Friendly!) Eating, 2022).

This resource provides cooking tips and delicious recipes tailored to individuals with ADHD. You can use this in addition to the "ADHD Friendly Eating Guide." Incorporating this guide can allow you to create a more ADHD-friendly meal plan that supports your child's overall well-being.

Comprehensive Guide to ADHD Medication

ADDitude also provides valuable resources, including The Ultimate Guide to ADHD Medication (2019). This resource can also be downloaded at additudemag.com.

Medication is a vital component of ADHD management for many families. This comprehensive guide offers in-depth information about various ADHD medications, their benefits, potential side effects, and how they work. This guide is readily available so that you can make well-informed decisions regarding your child's medication regimen.

Exploring Natural ADHD Treatment Options

ADDitude provides a Free Guide to Natural ADHD Treatment Options, which can be downloaded at additudemag.com (Barrow, K. & Michaels, P., 2023).

If you're interested in exploring alternative or complementary ADHD treatments, this resource is a valuable starting point. It outlines various natural approaches to managing ADHD symptoms, providing insights into dietary changes, supplements, and lifestyle adjustment. This guide in print allows you to refer to it whenever you seek non-pharmacological solutions.

Kid-Friendly Mindful Meditation Exercises

Research from ADDitude explains how mindfulness and meditation exercises improve symptoms of ADHD. The guide can be obtained from additudemag.com (deBros, K., Willard, C., & Buck, E., 2023).

This source will help you discover ADHD-friendly meditation exercises to incorporate into your child's daily routine. Acquiring and practicing these exercises can allow your child to engage more actively in mindfulness practices.

These resources are readily accessible online, and downloading and printing them can serve as tangible reminders and references for your ADHD management journey. Remember, progress may not always be immediate or linear, but your commitment to finding the best treatment options for your child is commendable. As you equip yourself with knowledge and strategies, you pave the way for positive changes in your child's life.

In the words of Lailah G. Akita, "Do not worry about who gets the credit or praise for the work done. Continue to work to give your best. Your reward may come unexpected." Your dedication to your child's well-being and the resources at your disposal are powerful tools on this rewarding path. As you explore treatments, engage in training, and possibly attend family therapy, you'll be well-prepared to nurture stronger bonds and open lines of communication within your family, fostering a supportive and loving environment for your child's growth and development.

Chapter 4
Talk to and Bond With Your Neurodivergent Child

When parenting a neurodivergent child, two crucial elements often stand at the forefront: communication and emotional bonding. This chapter is a beacon of guidance, revealing the path to stronger connections between parents and their children. With an unwavering focus on enhancing communication and nurturing profound emotional bonds, we set out on a transformative exploration.

It's vital to acknowledge that neurodivergent ADHD children exhibit a spectrum of symptoms, ranging from mild to moderate, with a minority experiencing severe challenges (ADHD Statistics: New ADD Facts and Research, 2006). Research also shows that a significant percentage of these remarkable children grapple with speech and language issues (Al-Dakroury, WA., 2018). As we delve into the heart of this chapter, let's remember that establishing effective communication and fostering emotional closeness is the cornerstone upon which we can build positive behavior reinforcement and nurture routines.

Navigating the unique parenting approach to neurodiversity encompasses understanding, empathy, and patience. As a parent, it is within your power to create an environment where your child feels seen, heard, and cherished. The exercises and strategies in the sections below are tools and opportunities for you to engage with your child meaningfully. Imagine the joy of connecting with your neurodivergent child on a deeper level, discovering their inner world, and building a bond that transcends the barriers imposed by ADHD. Picture the resilience, confidence, and self-esteem that will blossom within them as they experience unwavering support from you, their parent, guide, and advocate. Together, let's embark on this enlightening journey of connection and growth.

Effective Communication: A Compass for Connection

For parents of neurodivergent children, particularly those with ADHD, effective communication takes center stage. As we embark on this journey to enhance communication with your child, we'll uncover invaluable strategies and techniques to allow understanding, nurture your bond, and pave the way for a smoother daily life. The ADHD Center provides valuable insights in their article Some Communication Strategies for Parents of Kids with ADHD (2019).

Understanding the Unique Challenges

Before we dive into the strategies that will revolutionize your interactions with your ADHD child, we must grasp their unique challenges in this journey. Setting unrealistic expectations can inadvertently lead to frustration. Recognize that attention spans may vary widely, and what seems obvious to you may not always be apparent to your child. It is crucial to bridge this gap effectively by stepping into their shoes, even momentarily, to comprehend their perspective and adapt to communication accordingly.

The reality is that children with ADHD often experience difficulties with executive functions, which include attention, impulse control, and organization. These functions can impact communication in various ways, such as impulsive responses or a tendency to become easily distracted. As a parent, your role is to create a supportive and nurturing environment that considers these challenges.

The Power of Simplicity

Communication in ADHD requires simplicity. Providing short and straightforward directions can help prevent your child from becoming overwhelmed. Complex instructions can be challenging for ADHD children to process. Imagine offering a clear and concise road map, enabling them to navigate tasks effortlessly. Remember, clarity is your ally in effective communication. Consider breaking down tasks into manageable steps and using visual cues like checklists or schedules to guide your child through their responsibilities. This approach enhances understanding and empowers your child to take ownership of their actions.

Visual Aids and Nonverbal Cues

Visual aids are potent tools in the ADHD communication arsenal. They transform abstract concepts into tangible, understandable images. Visual cues, such as charts, schedules, or pictograms, serve as reliable guides for your child, enhancing their memory, comprehension, and engagement.

Imagine a scenario where your child's morning routine involves getting dressed, brushing their teeth, and packing their school bag. Instead of relying solely on verbal instructions, you can create a visual checklist featuring each task's images or drawings. This simple yet effective tool empowers your child to follow the routine, remember to perform minor tasks, and independently foster a sense of accomplishment.

Nonverbal cues also play a pivotal role in facilitating communication. Gestures, facial expressions, and body language convey emotions and intentions effectively, bridging potential communication gaps. Your calm and composed demeanor and nonverbal cues can bring reassurance, even in challenging moments.

Empowering With Choices

ADHD children often thrive when given a sense of control. Offering choices empowers them to participate actively in decision-making. This not only enhances their engagement but also reduces resistance. For instance, asking whether they'd like to complete homework before or after enjoying a favorite activity grants them a sense of agency within established boundaries.

By incorporating choices into your communication, you provide opportunities for your child to exercise their decision-making skills while still adhering to essential routines and responsibilities. This balance encourages a sense of independence and cooperation.

The Role of Behavioral Therapy

Behavioral therapy communication strategies are a valuable resource in nurturing effective interactions. Specific techniques, such as "when/then" statements, prove remarkably effective. These statements provide clarity about expectations and rewards, reinforcing positive behavior. For example,

"When you finish your homework, then you can play baseball." This approach can improve communication with your entire family, not just your ADHD child.

Behavioral therapy also encompasses the principles of positive reinforcement. By acknowledging and rewarding desired behaviors, you create a motivating environment. Praise, small incentives, or privileges can serve as effective rewards, motivating your child to make positive choices in their daily life.

Addressing Common Communication Challenges

Effective communication hinges on addressing everyday challenges. Recognize when you or your child may be talking excessively, interrupting, or struggling to find the right words. It's essential to develop strategies to manage these hurdles effectively. Let's look at some of the communication issues you may face:

- Talking Too Much: Sometimes, we elaborate rather than keep things concise. Encourage yourself to express thoughts succinctly, making your messages more accessible.
- Interruptions: Interrupting conversations can disrupt the flow of communication. Practice active listening and rehearse, not interrupting, to create a respectful and attentive atmosphere. Your child will learn from your actions.
- At a Loss for Words: When words fail you or your child, embrace alternative forms of expression. Encourage nonverbal communication through gestures, drawing, or writing to convey thoughts and feelings effectively. Also, allow them some time to rest

and allow their memory time to bring forth the words to express themselves.

- Going Off Topic: Off-topic conversations when discussing other things can be expected. Implement techniques to steer discussions back to the matter at hand, ensuring clarity and focus.
- Distractions: In an era of constant distractions, staying focused can be challenging. Employ techniques like setting a timer for brief, focused discussions and using visual or auditory cues to signal attention.
- Impulsivity and Emotional Reactions: Emotional reactions can sometimes hinder communication. Cultivate mindfulness and emotional regulation strategies to maintain composure during conversations. Encourage your child to do the same.
- Being Misunderstood: Misunderstandings will occur, but they need not derail communication. Teach your child active listening skills, ensuring both parties fully grasp the intended message.

Effective ADHD communication is a skill that evolves with practice, understanding, and patience. Applying these strategies and addressing common communication challenges will create an environment where your child feels heard, respected, and empowered. This newfound connection will lay the foundation for positive interactions, nurtured self-esteem, and resilience in your neurodivergent child. The journey begins with understanding, simple yet powerful strategies, and a commitment to maintaining a nurturing and communicative relationship.

Fostering a Flourishing Self-Esteem and Strong Social Bonds in Your Child

Navigating the terrain of parenting, especially when raising a neurodivergent child with ADHD, presents a unique set of challenges. The most notable being low self-esteem and difficulty with social skills. Various research has been done on how ADHD affects a child's self-esteem.

The Link Between ADHD and Low Self-Esteem

Understanding the relationship between ADHD and self-esteem is the cornerstone of effective parenting, and research provides insights into the link between them (Marais, 2022). As stated earlier, children with ADHD often struggle with lower self-esteem. This can be attributed to several factors, including difficulties in academic performance, social interactions, and emotional regulation. Children with ADHD often feel that no one understands them, making them feel isolated and different. The manifestation of ADHD symptoms, such as forgetfulness or impulsivity, can lead to feelings of inadequacy and self-doubt.

"Be patient with me. Understand why I do the things I do. Don't yell at me. Believe me, I don't want to have ADHD."

– Joane E Richardson

Recognizing this intricate connection is the first step toward creating a nurturing environment that uplifts your child's self-esteem. By acknowledging and proactively addressing the

challenges they face, you can empower your child to develop a
healthy self-image.

Boosting Self-Esteem Through Conscious Connections

Building your child's self-esteem begins with conscious and
intentional efforts. Here are essential strategies that can guide
you on this journey:

- Recognize Their Efforts: Acknowledging and
  affirming your child's efforts, no matter how small, is a
  potent way to boost self-esteem. Celebrate their
  achievements and praise their determination. This
  recognition communicates that their actions are
  valued and appreciated, creating a sense of
  accomplishment.
- Connect Consciously: Building a connection with
  your child involves active listening, empathy, and an
  open heart. Take the time to truly engage with them,
  showing genuine interest in their thoughts, feelings,
  and experiences. Ask open-ended questions that
  invite them to share their perspectives and emotions.
- Parental Reflective Functioning: Parental reflective
  functioning is valuable for understanding your child's
  inner world. It involves empathizing with their
  thoughts and emotions, even when they may not
  express them explicitly. Cultivating this skill can
  foster mutual respect and gain your child's trust.
- Look for Mirror Traits: ADHD often confers unique
  strengths and talents. Recognizing these mirror traits
  is essential. Your child may possess remarkable
  creativity, resilience, or problem-solving abilities.
  Identifying and nurturing these traits can significantly
  contribute to their self-esteem.

- Articulate and Empathize with Challenges:
  Acknowledge your child's challenges and difficulties.
  Express empathy by articulating that you
  understand their struggles. This validation helps
  your child feel heard and supported. It can also
  teach you the art of patience as you navigate these
  challenges together.

Incorporating these strategies into your daily interactions
creates a nurturing atmosphere that boosts self-esteem. Your
child begins to perceive themselves as capable and valued,
empowering them to tackle life's challenges with resilience and
confidence.

Strengthening Social Skills Through Connection

Social skills are vital to a child's development and play a crucial
role in building self-esteem. Children with ADHD may face
specific social challenges, such as difficulty with impulse
control or maintaining attention during conversations.
Nurturing these skills is an integral part of the journey.
HealthCentral provides valuable resources in their article 9
Ways to Teach Your Child Empathy (2014) to assist and guide
parents in the journey to social skills and ADHD.

- Empathetic Listening: Encourage your child to
  practice compassionate listening by actively engaging
  in conversations with peers and family members.
  Teach them the importance of understanding other's
  perspectives and emotions, which fosters meaningful
  connections.
- Role-Playing: Role-playing scenarios can be an
  effective way to practice social interactions. Create
  situations where your child can navigate various social

challenges, such as initiating conversations, sharing, or resolving conflicts.

- Social Groups and Activities: Enroll your child in social groups or activities that align with their interests. These environments provide opportunities to develop social skills while engaging in enjoyable experiences.
- Setting Social Goals: Collaboratively set social goals with your child. These goals include initiating conversations, maintaining eye contact, or taking turns during play. Regularly assess progress and celebrate achievements.
- Teach Problem-Solving: Empower your child with problem-solving skills that enable them to navigate social challenges effectively. Encourage them to identify solutions and evaluate the consequences of their actions.

By focusing on these strategies, you nurture your child's social skills and bolster their self-esteem. As they navigate social interactions with greater confidence and competence, their self-image becomes more positive and resilient.

By understanding the intricate connection between ADHD and self-esteem, you can initiate a path of empowerment and conscious connection. Recognize your child's efforts, connect with empathy, and cultivate their unique strengths. Through these deliberate efforts, you enable self-esteem and social skills that will serve as invaluable assets throughout their lives. Remember, the bond you forge today will shape your child's future, built on resilience, confidence, and unwavering self-worth.

Nurturing Social Skills and Communication Through Play

Parenting is not just about teaching and guiding; it's also about connecting and bonding with your child. One of the most effective ways to improve your child's social and communication skills is through engaging in fun activities. This section will explore games and interactive activities that reinforce these vital skills and strengthen the parent-child bond.

The Cook-Off: A Culinary Adventure

Cooking is a wonderful way to engage your child's creativity, teamwork, and communication skills. The cook-off game offers a delightful culinary experience and allows your child to express themselves, make choices, and collaborate. Here's how to cook up some fun:

1. Choose a Formula: Select a simple recipe you and your child can follow. Opt for dishes that allow room for creativity, such as homemade pizza or build-your-own tacos.
2. Select Ingredients: Involve your child in selecting ingredients for the chosen dish. Encourage them to express their preferences and make choices.
3. Work as a Team: While cooking, emphasize the importance of working together. Assign tasks that require coordination, like chopping vegetables or spreading sauce.
4. Communicate: Throughout the process, engage in conversations with your child. Encourage them to ask questions, share their thoughts, and express their

feelings. This open communication fosters social skills and enhances bonding.

5. Enjoy the Meal: After cooking, sit down and savor the meal you both prepared. Use this time to discuss the experience, what went well, and what could be improved next time.

The cook-off not only strengthens communication but also promotes cooperation and self-expression. It's a delicious way to connect with your child while nurturing essential life skills. Don't forget to have fun!

Stargazing: Exploring the Cosmos Together

Stargazing offers a captivating opportunity to bond with your child while encouraging curiosity and conversation. This activity stimulates their imagination and allows them to develop observational and communication skills. Here's how to engage in this celestial adventure:

1. Prepare for Stargazing: Choose a clear evening and find a suitable location away from city lights. Lay out a blanket or set up comfortable chairs for both you and your child.
2. Observe the Stars: Lie down and gaze at the night sky together. Encourage your child to point out constellations, stars, and any other celestial objects they find intriguing.
3. Ask Questions: Spark conversations by asking open-ended questions. For example: "What do you think stars are made of?" or "If you could visit any planet, which one would it be?"
4. Share Stories: Share myths, legends, or interesting facts about the stars and constellations. This

storytelling element adds depth to the experience and fosters curiosity.

5. Capture the Moment: Consider bringing a notebook or sketchbook to document your stargazing adventure. Encourage your child to draw what they see or jot down their thoughts and observations.

Stargazing provides a serene bonding experience and cultivates your child's communication and observational skills. It encourages them to ask questions, share their thoughts, and explore the wonders of the universe together.

Arts and Crafts Project: Unleashing Creativity Together

Engaging in arts and crafts projects is a fantastic way to stimulate creativity, fine-tune motor skills, and improve communication. This activity promotes self-regulation and patience while allowing your child to express themselves artistically. Here's how to start this artistic masterpiece:

1. Choose a Project: Select an arts and crafts project that aligns with your child's interests and skill level. Whether painting, drawing, or crafting, ensure it's an enjoyable activity for both of you.
2. Gather Supplies: Collect all the necessary materials, from paints and brushes to paper or crafting supplies. Organize them neatly to facilitate the creative process.
3. Collaborate: Work on the project together. Encourage your child to share their ideas, colors, and techniques. Discuss the project's theme or concept as you create.
4. Focus on Self-Expression: Emphasize the importance of self-expression through art. Encourage your child to express their feelings, thoughts, or stories through their artwork.

5. Celebrate Creations: Celebrate your artistic achievements once the project is complete. Display the artwork or create a dedicated gallery space to showcase your creations.

Engaging in arts and crafts projects fosters open communication, creativity, and collaboration. It's an opportunity to bond while nurturing your child's artistic talents and self-expression.

The Weekend Adventure: Exploring the World Together

Weekend adventures provide an excellent learning, exploration, and bonding platform. Children with ADHD often thrive in dynamic, interactive settings where they can engage with their surroundings. Here's how to plan and have your weekend adventure:

1. Plan the Adventure: Collaborate with your child to plan an adventure that aligns with their interests. Whether hiking, visiting a museum, or exploring a local park, involve them in the decision-making process.
2. Engage in Discovery: As you start the adventure, encourage your child to explore, ask questions, and engage with their surroundings—cultivating curiosity by discussing exciting discoveries.
3. Converse on the Go: Maintain an open line of communication throughout the adventure. Ask questions about what your child is experiencing, what they find fascinating, or any challenges they encounter.
4. Problem-Solve: If challenges arise during the adventure, use them as opportunities to teach

problem-solving skills. Collaborate with your child to find solutions and overcome obstacles.

5. Reflect and Share: After the adventure, take time to reflect and share your experiences. Discuss memorable moments, lessons learned, and what you both enjoyed about the adventure.

Weekend adventures offer a dynamic setting for communication, exploration, and problem-solving. They encourage your child to engage with their environment while strengthening your parent-child bond actively.

Musical Chairs: A Rhythmic Social Activity

Games can be powerful tools for developing social skills and communication. Musical chairs, with soft music, is a fun and exciting activity that promotes social interaction and decision-making. Here's how to set this up and start this interactive game:

1. Arrange the Chairs: Set up chairs in a circle, with one less chair than there are participants, including you and your child.
2. Start the Music: Play soft, upbeat music your child enjoys. Encourage them to walk around the circle of chairs while the music plays.
3. Stop the Music: Pause the music at intervals. When the music stops, everyone must quickly find a chair to sit in.
4. Discuss Small Moments: During a pause in the game, initiate discussions about the game's rules, strategies, and decision-making. Encourage your child to share their thoughts and ideas.

5. Rotate Roles: Switch between controlling the music and participating in the game. This rotation promotes leadership skills and cooperative play.

Musical chairs provide an enjoyable social activity and encourages communication, decision-making, and teamwork. It's a playful way to reinforce social skills in your child.

Albert Mehrabian once said, "It's not only what you say but how you say it" (Dunbar, 2022). This statement holds profound significance when nurturing social and communication skills in your child. How you communicate through gestures and actions determines the effectiveness of your interactions. Remember that social skills and communication are intertwined; modeling these skills can be one of the most impactful ways to teach them.

To further reinforce these skills, it's essential to incorporate routines into your home environment. Consistency provides stability and predictability, which can particularly benefit children with ADHD. Establishing a daily routine with dedicated one-on-one time for these interactive activities ensures they become integral to your child's development.

In summary, nurturing social skills and communication is not only about imparting knowledge; it's about creating memorable experiences. These interactive games and activities are powerful tools for bonding, fostering self-esteem, and developing essential life skills. Through the playful exploration of the world and open communication, you guide your child and go on a shared adventure of growth and connection.

Chapter 5
Institute Structure to Welcome Peace into Your Home

As a parent raising a neurodivergent child with ADHD, there exist unique challenges that require a map to navigate effectively. This chapter will delve into the importance of structure as a foundational element that can bring harmony and peace into your home.

Neurodivergent children often encounter difficulties with self-control due to differences in brain functioning. Structure and routine provide them with external control. Establishing external control mechanisms is vital and empowers your child to thrive (Low, 2023).

Routines offer predictability and security. They will be our focus as we explore practical steps to create tailored routines for your child, from morning rituals to bedtime routines. Additionally, we'll delve into strategies to reduce sensory triggers and overload, creating a sensory-friendly environment within your home. With the proper structure, your home can become a sanctuary where your child can flourish, providing peace and harmony for your entire family.

Understanding Sensory Overload and Its Connection to ADHD

Sensory overload can be an overwhelming experience for children with ADHD, often exacerbating their emotional regulation and focus challenges. This section explores effective strategies to identify, understand, and mitigate sensory overload in your child's environment. By addressing this critical aspect of ADHD management, you can create a more comfortable and conducive space for your child to thrive. Verywell Health's article on what causes sensory overload in ADHD provides valuable information in effectively identifying and managing this challenge (Burch, 2023).

Sensory overload, a common concern for individuals with ADHD, occurs when sensory input overwhelms their nervous system's ability to process and filter information effectively. It's especially significant for those who may already struggle with daily sensory processing. Some children with ADHD may also have comorbid sensory processing disorder (SPD), making sensory overload even more challenging to manage and leading to symptoms that may initially appear similar to ADHD.

Recognizing the symptoms of sensory overload is essential. It can manifest as irritability, restlessness, difficulty concentrating, meltdowns, or even physical discomfort. The child can often experience temperature-related issues, such as getting cold quickly or being exceptionally sensitive to heat. As parents, recognizing these signs early empowers you to intervene effectively. Therefore, familiarize yourself with the telltale signs of sensory overload, such as heightened sensitivity to lights, sounds, textures, or smells and increased emotional reactivity.

Identifying and Addressing Sensory Overload Triggers

Identifying the culprits or triggers behind sensory overload is the first step in managing this issue. It's comparable to solving a puzzle unique to your child. Pinpointing these triggers may require careful observation, focusing on situations, environments, or stimuli that consistently provoke sensory overload in your child. Is it loud noises, crowded places, specific textures, or bright lights? Identifying these triggers provides valuable insights into crafting tailored solutions. Here are some common examples:

- Auditory Triggers: For some children, loud noises, such as the blaring of car horns or even the din of a bustling classroom, can be overwhelming. They may react with distress, covering their ears or becoming agitated.
- Visual Overstimulation: Bright lights or busy visual environments, like crowded shopping malls, can be overwhelming. Your child might become anxious or irritated in such settings.
- Tactile Sensitivities: Some children have heightened sensitivities to certain textures or sensations. Tags in clothing, seams of socks, or the feeling of certain fabrics against their skin can lead to sensory overload. Consider your child's temperature sensitivities when deciding on tactile and textures, as some children may be more sensitive to cold or heat.
- Smell and Taste Sensitivities: Unpleasant or strong odors and specific tastes or food textures can trigger sensory overload. Your child may respond by gagging, refusing to eat, or becoming extremely distressed.

- Emotional Triggers: Sensory overload can also be triggered by emotional factors, such as stress, frustration, or anxiety. These emotional states can heighten sensory sensitivities, making the environment feel even more overwhelming.

Reducing Sensory Triggers

Once you've identified the triggers, the next step is to reduce exposure to them. Creating a structured routine that your child expects can be remarkably effective. Consistency in daily activities helps your child anticipate and prepare for sensory challenges, reducing the element of surprise that often leads to overload. Additionally, adjusting the home environment can make a world of difference. Simple modifications, such as using sensory aids like noise-canceling headphones or providing a designated sensory-friendly space, can significantly reduce exposure to triggers.

Consider incorporating sensory-friendly additives into your child's routine. These can include using weighted blankets, fidget toys, or even aromatic aids like a container of soothing scents. These tools can provide a comforting sensory experience, helping to mitigate overload.

Teaching Relaxation Techniques and Seeking Support

Empowering your child with relaxation techniques is a valuable skill to help them manage sensory overload more effectively. Techniques like deep-breathing exercises, progressive muscle relaxation, or mindfulness activities can equip your child with the tools to self-regulate and soothe their overwhelmed nervous system. Practicing these techniques together can also be an excellent bonding opportunity.

Remember, learning the triggers and how to reduce sensory overload is a journey that may require patience and experimentation. Seek support from professionals or support groups specializing in ADHD and sensory issues. They can offer guidance, share experiences, and provide additional resources tailored to your child's unique needs. With understanding and proactive strategies, you can create an environment that nurtures your child's well-being, reducing sensory overload's impact and enhancing their overall quality of life.

Addressing sensory overload is an essential component of managing ADHD in your child. Recognizing the signs, identifying triggers, and implementing practical strategies can significantly reduce its impact on your child's daily life.

Managing Sensory Overload

As stated above, sensory overload can be particularly challenging for children with ADHD. Understanding how to manage sensory overloads and triggers is crucial to helping your child navigate their environment more comfortably.

Hyperactivity

For hyperactive children with ADHD, engaging in physical activities that provide sensory input can be beneficial. Encourage them to help with tasks like carrying the laundry basket, pushing the shopping cart, or bringing grocery bags from the car. These activities channel their excess energy and give them a sense of accomplishment and control over their sensory experiences.

Additionally, consider incorporating movement breaks into their daily routine. Activities like jumping on a trampoline, using a therapy swing, or engaging in these exercises can help regulate their sensory systems and reduce the risk of sensory overload.

Tactile Sensitivity

Children with tactile sensitivities often struggle with textures and sensations. You can introduce activities that provide a controlled sensory experience to address this. For example, finger-painting activities at the kitchen table allow your child to explore different textures in a controlled environment.

Incorporating sensory-friendly materials like shaving cream into bath time can also be helpful. Let your child draw pictures on the walls with the shaving cream, creating a fun and engaging sensory experience. Another option is to fill a plastic bin with dry beans or rice and hide small toys inside. Your child can then explore and discover these hidden treasures while becoming more accustomed to different tactile sensations.

Fear of Loud Noises

Children terrified of loud noises may require unique strategies to help them cope with sensory overload in noisy situations. One creative approach is to have a "rainstorm party." Bring pots and pans during this activity and encourage your child to create thunder-like sounds. This can work exceptionally well during a thunderstorm where your child can be invited to "beat the thunder first" or "bang louder than the thunder."

This approach allows your child to take control of the situation, turning something frightening into a playful and engaging activity. It helps them desensitize to loud noises and builds their confidence in managing sensory challenges.

Food Sensitivities

Some children with ADHD have a strong aversion to certain foods due to sensory issues. To help them expand their palate and accommodate their sensory preferences, consider preparing the disliked foods in new ways. For example, if your child dislikes the texture of cooked peas, try meshing them and incorporating them into stews or meatloaf. This modification changes the sensory experience of the food, making it more palatable for your child.

Additionally, involve your child in the meal preparation process. Let them explore different foods, touch ingredients, and even participate in cooking when appropriate. This hands-on approach can help them learn new textures and flavors. Encourage them to express their preferences and be patient as they gradually become more comfortable with a broader range of foods.

Oral Sensitivities

Children with oral sensitivities may have difficulty with certain textures or oral movements. To address these challenges, offer your child sugarless gum or chewy, healthy treats that require increased jaw movement. Ensure they brush their teeth afterward or rinse with water to maintain oral hygiene.

Another helpful strategy is to have your child drink thick shakes through a straw. This stimulates oral movement and allows them to become more accustomed to different sensations in the mouth. Gradually introduce a variety of textures and temperatures, such as smoothies, yogurt, or frozen fruit bars, to encourage sensory exploration.

Sensitivity to Clothing

Some children with ADHD can become easily irritated by clothing, mainly clothing tags and seams. If your child is bothered by labels sewn inside their clothing, consider purchasing tops and pants without these tags. Some manufacturers, like Fun and Function, offer tagless items with flat seams specially washed to feel natural against the skin. These clothing options can significantly reduce discomfort for sensitive children. When your child is at an age where they can be taught to remove labels from their clothing in a safe way, it is to their future benefit to learn how to remove tags themselves.

Allow your child to choose comfortable clothing and consider their preferences regarding fabric types and clothing styles. By accommodating their sensory needs and preferences, you can help them feel more at ease in their everyday attire.

It's essential to approach these sensory challenges with empathy and patience. Sensory sensitivities can vary widely among children with ADHD, and what works for one child may not work for another. Be open to trying different strategies and techniques to find the best ways to support your child in overcoming sensory challenges and enhancing their overall well-being.

Helping Your Child Relax and De-Stress

Children with ADHD often face moments of being overwhelmed and heightened stress levels. Teaching them relaxation techniques can be a valuable skill for managing these emotions. These techniques can be adapted and modified as your child ages to ensure they remain effective.

- Guided Breath Techniques: One of the simplest and most effective ways to help your child relax is guided breathing techniques. Teach them to take slow, deep breaths in a controlled manner. For example, you can encourage them to inhale deeply for a count of four, hold their breath for four counts, and then exhale slowly for four counts. This rhythmic breathing pattern can help calm their nervous system and reduce feelings of anxiety. As they age, you can introduce more advanced breathing exercises to further enhance their self-regulating and de-stressing ability.

- EFT Tapping: Emotional Freedom Techniques (EFT) tapping is powerful for managing stress and anxiety. It involves tapping specific acupressure points on the body while verbalizing feelings and affirmations. This technique has shown promise in reducing stress and improving emotional well-being. Encourage your child to try EFT tapping when they feel overwhelmed. Many online resources and videos are available to guide them through the process. As your child becomes more familiar with EFT, they can customize their tapping routines to address specific emotions or situations.

- Binaural Beats: Binaural beats are a form of auditory therapy that can help induce relaxation and reduce anxiety. You can compile a playlist of binaural beats and music and keep it accessible on your laptop or phone. When stressed, your child can listen to these beats through headphones to encourage relaxation. Binaural beats play slightly different frequencies in each ear, creating a calming and soothing effect in the brain. They can also assist with focus and concentration, making them a valuable tool for children with ADHD.

- Barefoot Stroll: Spending time outdoors and connecting with nature can be therapeutic for children with ADHD. Encourage your child to stroll barefoot in the grass or on a sandy beach. Walking barefoot can help ground their energy and reduce feelings of restlessness. This simple yet effective activity allows them to connect with the earth and experience sensory input from different textures underfoot. It's a great way to promote relaxation and mindfulness.

- Quick Massage: Applying essential oils to specific body parts, such as the wrists or behind the ears, can create a calming sensory experience for your child. Essential oils like lavender, orange, chamomile, and others are known for their stress-reducing and mood-enhancing properties. You can even blend different oils to create a customized soothing aroma. Massaging these oils onto your child's skin can provide a comforting and grounding sensation. This practice can help them manage stress and improve their overall mood.

Teaching these relaxation techniques to your child empowers them with valuable coping strategies for managing stress and overwhelming emotions. Incorporating these methods into their daily routine can create a supportive environment that promotes emotional well-being and self-regulation.

Instituting Routines and Schedules: A Blueprint for Success

Establishing routines and schedules in the daily lives of children with ADHD is a pivotal strategy for managing their symptoms, enhancing their well-being, and promoting academic and social success. These children often struggle with executive functions, self-regulation, and time management.

Hence, routines can provide a sense of external control, helping them navigate their world more effectively. This comprehensive guide delves into the significance of structured routines and their numerous benefits. It offers practical insights into adapting and implementing consistency that cater to your child's unique needs.

Routines are the cornerstone of effective ADHD management. They bring structure and predictability to a child's day, mitigating the chaos and impulsivity often associated with ADHD. A well-established routine helps children feel more secure, focused, and successful. It reduces anxiety and provides a clear framework for daily activities. Research shows that children with ADHD thrive in environments that incorporate routines into their daily lives.

The Benefits of Routines

The advantage of implementing routines extends far beyond merely organizing a child's day. It impacts various aspects of life, including academic performance, emotional regulation, and family harmony. Offering the following benefits:

- Enhanced Time Management: Routines help children allocate their time more efficiently, reducing procrastination and last-minute rushes.
- Improved Focus and Attention: Predictable routines enable ADHD children to concentrate better on tasks, as they know what to expect next.
- Emotional Regulation: Routines reduce stress and anxiety by providing a stable, confronting environment that supports emotional regulation.
- Independence: Children develop a sense of independence and self-confidence when they can

manage their daily activities through established
routines.

- Consistency in Behavioral Expectations: Routines set
  clear expectations for behavior, reducing impulsivity
  actions and temper outbursts.

Adaptation to Your Child's Needs and Triggers

While routines are undeniably beneficial, it's crucial to
customize them to suit your child's unique needs, triggers, and
executive functions. Consider your child's personality,
sensitivities, and specific challenges when designing routines.
Flexibility is vital, as what works today might need adjustments
tomorrow.

Maintain Routine Throughout the Day

To provide a comprehensive structure for your child, create
routines that span the entire day, including morning, after-
school, and bedtime routines. Adjusting these as your child
grows and matures. However, always maintain a balance
between structure and flexibility. Children with ADHD may
become overwhelmed if routines are too rigid, so allow for some
adaptability.

Use Reminders, Timers, and Digital Tools

Employ various tools and strategies to support your child in
adhering to their routines. Written schedules are an excellent
visual aid for children with ADHD. Additionally, consider
using reminders and timers to help them remember tasks and
transitions. Digital apps like Simple Mind Pro and Evernote
can be invaluable tools for organizing schedules and to-do lists.
These apps provide flexibility and accessibility, ensuring your
child has their schedule at their fingertips whenever needed.

Utilize Remember the Milk App

One valuable tool in managing routines for ADHD children is the Remember the Milk app. This app is beneficial because it enables you to create task lists and reminders for daily activities. You can organize tasks into categories, set priorities, and establish deadlines. This level of organization can be immensely beneficial for children with ADHD, as it helps them visualize their responsibilities and provides a sense of structure. This app allows you to break down complex tasks into smaller, more manageable subtasks. For instance, if your child has homework assignments, you can list each step required to complete them. This makes the tasks less daunting and enhances the child's sense of accomplishment as they check off each subtask.

Harness the Power of Visuals

Visual aids are indispensable when establishing routines for children with ADHD. Visuals provide a tangible and easy-to-understand representation of the day's schedule. Your child will be able to know precisely what tasks come next, check off assignments completed, and emotionally prepare for jobs that still need to be completed. This also provides clarity when used to break down larger tasks into smaller steps. It is a constant reminder, helping your child stay on track and manage their time effectively.

One effective visual tool is a daily routine chart. These charts display the activities or tasks that must be accomplished in a specific order throughout the day. Visual cues, such as images or icons, can be added to make the chart more engaging and easily comprehended, especially for younger children. For example, a morning routine chart may include waking up, brushing teeth, getting dressed, and having breakfast. Similarly, a bedtime routine chart could feature tasks like brushing teeth, reading a book, and getting into bed.

Creating Routine and Schedule Charts

Creating a routine and a schedule chart doesn't have to be a complex or time-consuming task. Various resources and templates are available online to simplify the process. One such resource is the Goally app, which offers free printable ADHD routine charts. These charts are pre-designed and ready to use, making it easier for parents to start. To create your routine chart, you can follow these basic steps:

- List Tasks: List all the tasks or activities that must be included in the routine. Consider the specific needs and preferences of your child.
- Sequence: Organize the tasks in the order they should be completed. Ensure the sequence makes sense and is conducive to a smooth routine flow.
- Add Visuals: Incorporate visual cues or icons next to each task to make the chart more visually appealing and user-friendly.
- Review and Adjust: Regularly review the routine with your child and make any necessary adjustments. This ensures that the practice remains effective and adaptable to changing circumstances.

Sample Routine

To provide an example, let's create a sample morning routine for your child with ADHD:

1. Wake Up: Image of a smiling sun.
2. Brush Teeth: Toothbrush icon.

3. Get Dressed: Clothing hanger image.
4. Have Breakfast: Plant with food icon.
5. Pack School Bag: Backpack illustration.

This visual routine chart offers a clear, simple, and engaging representation of the morning tasks. By following these steps, parents can help their children stay organized and independently manage their morning routine.

As you embark on this journey to enhance your child's life by optimizing routines and schedules, remember that you're taking significant steps to create an environment where they can flourish.

The tools and techniques you've learned in this chapter are valuable assets in providing your child with the structure and organization they need to succeed. However, this is just the beginning. The next phase of the *BEATITUDE* solution involves addressing your child's educational needs and instilling positive attitudes through reinforcement strategies.

In the words of Ed Reed: "Everyone has their greatness. Whether you reach your greatness depends on your environment, structure, the company you keep, and your attitude."

Chapter 6
Transform into Your Child's Educational Advocate

In the previous chapters, we delved into various aspects of supporting and understanding your neurodivergent child with ADHD. It's time to tackle the educational front with the same vigor and determination that has brought us this far. Did you know that 30% to 40% of children with ADHD require special education services and programs? Considering that 32% to 35% of students drop out of school during their teenage years, this is an equally concerning fact that highlights the importance of parental involvement in shaping the educational experiences of our children (Cooney, 2020). As parents, we hold the power to change these statistics and ensure our children receive the education and support they need to thrive.

The Impact of ADHD on Learning

While ADHD is commonly associated with symptoms like hyperactivity and impulsivity, it can also profoundly impact a child's learning abilities. As parents and educators advocate for children with ADHD, it's crucial to understand how this condition influences their educational experiences.

Let's delve deeper into the various challenges children with ADHD may encounter in school and how you can effectively advocate for their educational needs.

Increased Susceptibility to Boredom

Children with ADHD often struggle more with boredom and may find investing mental effort into tasks challenging. Whether they are engaged in virtual learning or attending classes in person, children with ADHD may lack the novelty and excitement that can help sustain their interest in education. This heightened susceptibility to boredom can impact their academic performance and overall engagement in the classroom.

Teachers play a pivotal role in addressing this challenge. Talk with them about new and creative ways they can keep children with ADHD engaged in learning. This can involve incorporating interactive activities, technology, and opportunities for movement and hands-on experiences.

Difficulty with Transitions

Transitions can be particularly challenging for children with ADHD. This difficulty extends beyond the classroom setting and can encompass various aspects of their daily lives. For instance, changing classes, going back and forth between different subjects or assignments, and shifting between schoolwork, homework, and family activities can be sources of stress and frustration for these children.

To mitigate these challenges, creating structured routines and providing clear expectations is essential. Additionally, offering support during transitions and allowing children to use tools like visual schedules and reminders can help them navigate these shifts more smoothly.

Executive Functioning Challenges

Executive functioning refers to cognitive processes that enable individuals to plan, organize, initiate tasks, manage time, and regulate their behavior effectively. Children with ADHD often face difficulties in these areas, making it challenging to stay organized and complete tasks efficiently.

In school, executive functioning challenges can manifest as forgetfulness, disorganization, difficulty prioritizing tasks, and impulsivity. These issues can impact academic performance and create frustration for the child and their educators. To address executive functioning challenges, parents and educators can collaborate to implement strategies such as making structured schedules, breaking tasks into smaller, manageable steps, and teaching organizational skills. Additionally, positive reinforcement and praise for completing tasks can help motivate children with ADHD.

Cognitive Functioning Difficulties

ADHD can affect various cognitive functions, including concentration, interaction, socialization, communication, and memorization. These cognitive challenges can hinder a child's ability to engage with peers, understand social concepts, and retain information.

In the classroom, children with ADHD may struggle to pay attention during lectures, participate in group discussions, and complete assignments that require sustained focus. They may also find it challenging to follow verbal instructions or remember essential details. To support children with ADHD in overcoming cognitive challenges, educators can implement strategies like visual aids, interactive learning activities, and frequent breaks. These accommodations can help children stay engaged and retain information more effectively.

Defiance, Risk-Taking Behaviors, and Opposition

An ADHD child may exhibit defiant behaviors, engage in risk-taking activities, and display oppositional tendencies. These behaviors can disrupt the learning environment and challenge teachers and parents.

Parents and educators must engage collaboratively to address these behaviors. This may involve implementing behavior management techniques, setting clear expectations and boundaries, and providing consequences and rewards for appropriate behavior.

Unique Executive Functioning

Children with ADHD have unique executive functioning profiles. Things such as hyperfocus and using visuals to remember things while helping organize their life. Their brains are wired differently from their neurotypical peers, and they may require individualized care and support within the school environment.

Educators must recognize and accommodate these differences. This may involve providing personalized instruction, offering extended time for assignments and tests, and considering alternative assessment methods that better align with the child's strengths.

Focusing on Key Areas

To effectively advocate for your child's education needs, it's essential to focus on critical areas of support and intervention. These areas include:

- Accessing Available Resources: Schools often offer services, such as special education programs, speech and language therapy, and occupational therapy, to assist children with ADHD. Collaborate with school staff to determine which resources most benefit your child's unique needs.
- Individualized Education Plans (IEPs) and 504 Plans: IEPs and 504 Plans are legal documents that outline the specific educational services and accommodations your child requires. Work with your child's school to create and regularly review their IEP or 504 plans to ensure they meet their evolving needs.
- Behavioral Interventions: Positive behavior support plans and interventions can help manage challenging behaviors associated with ADHD. Seek guidance from behavior specialists and educators to implement effective strategies.
- Communication and Collaboration: Maintain open and regular contact with your child's teachers, counselors, and school administrators. Collaboration between home and school is essential for addressing challenges and celebrating success.
- Advocacy Skills: Equip yourself with advocacy skills to navigate the educational system effectively. Attend workshops, conferences, and support groups to stay informed about your rights and your child's rights within the educational system.

Understanding the impact of ADHD on learning is a critical first step in advocating for your child's educational needs. By recognizing the challenges they face and working collaboratively with educators and support professionals, you can create a supportive and tailored learning environment that empowers your child to excel academically and thrive socially. Remember that every child with ADHD is unique, and finding the right combination of strategies and support is vital to their success.

Advocating for Your Child's Education: Navigating Individualized IEPs

As a parent of a child with ADHD, it is paramount to ensure your child receives the education they need to thrive. One of the most powerful tools at your disposal for achieving this goal is the Individualized Education Program (IEP). An IEP, as explained above, is a personalized plan designed to address your child's unique educational needs. It plays a crucial role in supporting their academic journey. This section will explore an IEP, its key components, and how to advocate effectively for your child's educational rights.

What Is an IEP?

An IEP is a legally binding document that outlines the specialized educational services and accommodations your child requires. It is specifically designed to meet the needs of students with disabilities, including those with ADHD. The IEP is a collaborative effort involving parents, educators, school administrators, and, in some cases, designated advocates. *Understanding IEPs* (n.d.) explains the intricate details and importance of understanding the steps and use of the IEP process.

The Eight Key Components of an IEP

To make the most of the IEP process and ensure your child receives the support they need, it's essential to understand the eight basic components of an IEP and determine your child's educational needs (Logsdon, 2022):

1. Current Skill Level: The IEP process begins with assessing your child's current skill level. This step helps identify their strengths and weaknesses, providing a foundation for setting appropriate goals.

2. Annual Goals: The IEP must specify your child's yearly goals, which should be updated at least once a year. These goals may relate to academic performance, behavior, physical mobility, and other areas relevant to your child's development.

3. Track Progress: The IEP must outline how your child's progress will be measured and reported. This section explains the methods and frequency of progress monitoring, ensuring parents and educators stay informed.

4. Special Educational Services, Classes, and Extras: The IEP should clearly define the special education services, classes, and additional support your child will receive. This includes details about specialized instruction, therapies, and any supplemental resources necessary for your child's success.

5. Duration of Service: Specify the timeline during which the proposed services and programs will take place. Understanding the duration of each service helps ensure continuity in your child's educational experience.

6. Mainstream Class Participation: This section addresses your child's inclusion in mainstream classes whenever appropriate. It outlines how and when your child will join regular education settings, promoting social integration.

7. Adaptations: If your child requires accommodations or modifications for standardized tests or assessments, the IEP must detail these adaptations. This ensures your child has equal opportunities to demonstrate their knowledge and abilities.

8. Transitional Goals: An IEP supports your child's current educational needs and prepares them for future educational phases. Starting around your child's 14th birthday, the IEP should include plans for transitioning beyond grade school, helping them navigate the path to higher education or employment.

How to Apply for an IEP

Obtaining an IEP involves several essential steps, and navigating the process effectively is crucial. Here's a general outline of how to apply for an IEP:

- Request an Evaluation: If you believe your child may need an IEP, the first step is to request an evaluation. Typically, this evaluation by the school assesses your child's strengths, weaknesses, and eligibility for special education services.

- Attend IEP Meetings: Once the evaluation is complete, you will participate in IEP meetings with school staff, including teachers, counselors, and administrators. These meetings are a collaborative platform to discuss your child's needs and develop the IEP.

- Review and Approve: Carefully review the proposed IEP to ensure it aligns with your child's requirements. If you have concerns or questions, don't hesitate to voice them during the meetings. Once you are satisfied with the plan, you can approve it.

- Implement and Monitor: After approval, the IEP is implemented, and your child will begin receiving the specified services and accommodations. Continuously monitor your child's progress to ensure the IEP effectively meets their needs.

Active Involvement in IEP Meetings

Your involvement in IEP meetings is crucial to advocating for your child's education rights. Here are some key tips for active participation:

- Know Your Child's Needs: Come prepared to clearly understand your child's strengths, weaknesses, and specific needs. Share this information with the IEP team to assist in developing the plan.
- Ask Questions: Don't hesitate to ask questions or seek clarification during the meetings. It's essential to fully understand the proposed IEP and how it will benefit your child.
- Collaborate with the Team: Approach IEP meetings as collaborative efforts with educators and support professionals. Foster open communication and a shared commitment to your child's success.
- Advocate for Your Child: Be a strong advocate for your child's rights and needs. Ensure that the IEP addresses all areas requiring support, from academics to social development.

Combatting Bullying: A Must-Have in the IEP

While advocating for your child's education needs, addressing other critical aspects of their school experience, including bullying prevention, is essential. Bullying can severely affect children with ADHD, affecting their emotional well-being and overall academic performance. Consider getting involved in initiatives and programs aimed at finding a safe way to handle bullying at school. Ensure your child's IEP includes provisions for creating a safe and supportive learning environment where bullying is actively addressed and prevented.

Empowering Your Child: Understanding 504 Accommodation Plans

In your journey to advocate for your child with ADHD, you may find that a 504 accommodation plan is another valuable resource to support their educational needs. This plan complements your advocacy efforts, providing additional assistance and ensuring that your child's educational environment is conducive to their success. This section will delve into what a 504 plan entails, how it differs from an IEP, and the critical components that make it effective.

What Is a 504 Plan?

A 504 plan, officially called a Section 504 accommodation plan, is a legal document designed to provide students with disabilities, including ADHD, equal access to education. It falls under Section 504 of the Rehabilitation Act of 1973 and the Americans with Disabilities Act (ADA). Unlike an IEP, which is tailored for students who require special education services, a 504 plan focuses on accommodations and modifications to level the playing field for students with disabilities.

How Does It Differ From an IEP?

While both 504 plans and IEPs serve students with disabilities, they have subtle yet significant differences:

- Eligibility: To qualify for an IEP, a student must meet specific criteria, often requiring more significant academic or developmental needs. In contrast, a 504 plan is available to students who have a disability that substantially limits one or more major life activities but may not require specialized instructions.
- Services: An IEP provides specialized education services tailored to a student's unique needs, such as individualized instructions or therapy. A 504 plan focuses on accommodations and modifications within the regular classroom to ensure equal access to learning.

What's Included in a 504 Plan?

A 504 plan typically includes various accommodations and modifications to remove barriers and provide students with disabilities access to learning. Some standard components of a 504 program include:

- Specific Accommodations: Accommodations address specific challenges your child faces, such as extended testing-taking time, preferential seating, or assistive technology such as speech-assisted devices.
- Environmental Adjustments: This can include changes to a learning environment, such as minimizing distractions or providing a quiet space for tasks requiring concentration.
- Individualized Support: Personalized support may include additional breaks and access to sensory tools

or strategies to manage impulsivity and attention challenges.

- Behavioral Interventions: This involves techniques to manage behaviors associated with ADHD, such as implementing a behavior plan or offering positive reinforcement.

How to Apply for a 504 Plan

Obtaining a 504 plan involves a structured process that ensures your child's needs are adequately addressed:

- Identification of a Disability: The first step is to establish that your child has a disability that substantially limits one or more major life activities. This typically involves a comprehensive evaluation.
- Request a 504 Evaluation: Reach out to your child's school or district for a 504 evaluation. This evaluation assesses your child's eligibility and identifies the accommodations they require.
- Participate in the 504 Meeting: A 504 meeting involving school staff and parents will be scheduled once eligibility is confirmed. Together, you will discuss your child's needs and develop the 504 plan.
- Review and Approve: Carefully review the proposed 504 plan and ensure it adequately addresses your child's requirements. Once satisfied, approve the plan.
- Implement and Monitor: The 504 plan is then implemented, with your child receiving the specified accommodations. Regular monitoring ensures the plan remains adequate.

Less Direct Involvement, Equally Important

Unlike IEPs, where parents play a more direct role in the planning and decision-making, 504 plans may not require the same level of involvement. However, they are equally vital for students with ADHD who may not require specialized instruction but still need accommodations to succeed in a regular classroom. It's crucial to stay informed and engaged in your child's educational journey. Regular communication with teachers and school staff can help ensure the plan effectively supports your child's needs.

Handling Bullying: A Vital Consideration

As with IEPs, addressing bullying prevention should be a critical component of your child's 504 plan. As mentioned, bullying affects mental well-being and academic success in all children, including children with ADHD. Advocate for measures within the plan that create a safe and inclusive learning environment.

Understanding the role of an accommodation plan in supporting your child with ADHD is essential for effective advocacy. While it differs from an IEP in its focus on accommodations rather than specialized instruction, it can provide vital support to ensure your child's educational success. By actively participating in the process, staying informed, and addressing concerns like bullying prevention, you empower your child to thrive academically and beyond. Every child deserves an environment where they can learn, grow, and reach their full potential.

Enhancing Socialization and Communication: The Role of Extra-Mural Activities for Children With ADHD

To support and empower children with ADHD, it's crucial to recognize the significance of extra-mural activities or after-school programs. These activities provide an avenue for children to expend their abundant energy and offer valuable opportunities for socialization, improved group interaction, and enhanced communication skills. This section will explore popular after-school activities that can significantly benefit children with ADHD and contribute to their overall development.

Scouting—Fostering Education and Fun

One after-school activity with tremendous potential for children with ADHD is scouting. Scouting programs, such as Boy Scouts and Girl Scouts, provide children with a structured environment where they can learn essential life skills while having fun. Scouting benefits children with ADHD in much the same way it benefits all children by offering education and enjoyable experiences. However, it's worth noting that certain scouting events may lack the structured routine that can be particularly beneficial for children with ADHD. Parents should consider discussing their child's needs with scouting leaders to ensure a supportive and accommodating experience.

Team Sports—Social Skills and Physical Activity

Participation in team sports is another excellent avenue for children with ADHD to develop social skills and engage in physical activities. Team sports promote cooperation, communication, and the ability to work harmoniously within a group. When selecting a sport for your child with ADHD, it's advisable to opt for activities that maintain a consistent level of physical activity, such as basketball or soccer. These sports often involve continuous movement and engagement, reducing the potential for downtime, which can be challenging for those children.

Art or Music Classes—Creativity and Expression

For children with ADHD, engaging in creative activities like art or music classes can be particularly beneficial. These activities provide a means for self-expression, creativity, and an outlet for their energy. Artistic pursuits can help children focus their attention and develop patience, which are essential skills for managing their ADHD symptoms. Moreover, these classes offer a sense of accomplishment as children see their artistic or musical abilities progress. The structured environment of art or music classes can provide the routine and discipline that complements ADHD management.

Reducing Screen Time—Prioritizing Physical Activity and Social Interactions

While considering extra-mural activities, it's crucial to address the issue of screen time. Excessive screen time, particularly after school, can impede a child's participation in physical and social activities. Parents can play a pivotal role in managing and reducing screen time, ensuring their child has ample opportunities to engage in after-school activities with peers or enjoy creative activities at home.

Encouraging physical play, outdoor exploration, and interactive games can help strike a balance between screen time and other activities. Setting clear boundaries and guidelines for screen use is essential in maintaining a healthy and active lifestyle for children with ADHD.

Collaboration with Schools: Empowering Your Child's Education

When it comes to ensuring the best possible education for children with ADHD, collaboration with the school system is an invaluable component of the BEATITUDE solution. Effective teamwork involves a proactive approach, consistent advocacy, and a commitment to working closely with educators to address your child's specific needs.

Why Collaboration Matters

Collaboration between parents and teachers is a cornerstone of ensuring the success and well-being of children with ADHD. This partnership fosters an environment where educators and caregivers work together to create tailored educational plans and support structures. There are several vital reasons collaboration matters:

- Understanding ADHD: Collaboration enables teachers to better understand ADHD, its symptoms, and its impact on your child's learning experience. When educators are well-informed about ADHD, they can implement strategies that cater to your child's specific needs.
- Individualized Education: By collaborating, you can contribute valuable insights about your child's behavior, preferences, and learning style. This information is crucial for designing IEPs and accommodations that align with your child's strengths and challenges.
- Consistency and Routine: Children with ADHD often thrive in structured environments with consistent routines. Collaborating with teachers can

help ensure that your child's daily schedule at school aligns with the routines established at home. This consistency can contribute to better focus and reduced anxiety.

- Effective Communication: Collaboration encourages open and effective communication between parents and educators. This communication is essential for sharing feedback, discussing progress, and addressing any concerns or challenges that may arise during your child's educational journey.

Collaboration in Action

To effectively collaborate with schools and educators, parents should engage on various levels and aspects of their child's education:

- Seating Arrangements: Collaborate with teachers on seating arrangements in the classroom. Children with ADHD may benefit from specific seating arrangements that minimize distractions and promote focus. Discussing this with teachers can lead to a more conducive learning environment.
- Homework Schedules: Establishing effective homework routines is crucial for children with ADHD. Collaborate with teachers to ensure that homework assignments are manageable and align with your child's capabilities. Maintaining mobile contact can be helpful for quick communication regarding homework-related issues.
- Transitions and Change: Children with ADHD often find transitions challenging. Collaborate with teachers and your child to develop strategies for managing

shifts and changes at home or school. Consistent approaches can help your child adapt more smoothly.

- Behavioral Issues: Addressing behavioral issues, including bullying, emotional dysregulation, rage, and meltdowns, requires teacher collaboration. Share your child's specific challenges and triggers and work together to develop strategies for managing and preventing these issues.
- Social Skills Development: Collaborate with educators to support your child's social skills development. Discuss techniques to encourage positive interactions with peers and how to address bullying when it occurs. Establish clear systems for addressing social challenges.

Interactive Element: Initiating Effective Collaboration

Consider preparing an initial questionnaire to kick-start effective collaboration with your child's teacher. This questionnaire can guide you during your first meeting and ensure that essential topics are covered. Here are sample questions to include:

- How familiar are you with ADHD? Have you had experience teaching children with this condition?
- Can I share specific details about my child's ADHD symptoms and behaviors to assist in designing an IEP?
- What strategies can I implement at home to encourage homework completion and participation in school activities?
- How often should we schedule feedback and collaboration meetings throughout the school year?

- Are there any specific accommodations or support services you recommend for my child?
- What teaching methods do you employ to engage children with ADHD and promote focus, interest, and motivation?
- Can you describe a typical classroom setting in action?
- What procedures are in place for addressing bullying, and what is the school's anti-bullying policy?
- Is there a designated time for unstructured activities or breaks during the school day?
- How can I be actively involved in supporting my child's education, and what is your preferred method of communication?

In the words of Natacha Buckmaster, "Sometimes in life, people are worth fighting for, and those that are, you will feel in your heart." Advocating for your child's educational needs at school is a way of fighting for their future, ensuring they receive the support and accommodations necessary for success. The benefits of proper education and individualized plans for children with ADHD far outweigh any efforts required for collaboration.

Chapter 7
Understanding and Reshaping Specific ADHD-Related Behaviors

E very parent faces the challenging task of managing and guiding their child's behavior. However, when parenting a child with ADHD, addressing different problematic behaviors can be complex. This chapter will explore managing problem behavior, offering a compassionate and practical approach that revolves around unique reinforcement strategies.

Did you know that, according to research by the CDC, 30% of parents use behavioral therapy to help their neurodivergent children develop improved behaviors? Reinforcement strategies are key to unlocking positive change in your child's behavior (*Behavior Therapy for Young Children With ADHD*, 2020). Focusing on strategies to help such behaviors will encourage positive choices in your child.

In navigating behavior challenges with neurodivergent children, it's essential to approach this journey with optimism, recognizing that with the right strategies and a supportive environment, positive changes are not only possible but achievable. Let's discover the transformative power of reinforcement strategies and their role in embracing the full spectrum of the *BEATITUDE* solution.

Nurturing Positive Behavior in Children With ADHD

Among the many aspects of caring for a child with ADHD, managing their behavior is often a central concern for parents. It's essential to approach this task with empathy, patience, and a deep understanding of the underlying factors contributing to ADHD-related behaviors. When we look into ADHD behavior, it is essential to emphasize that these behaviors are not "bad." Instead, they are a result of neurodivergent brain functions and chemical processes.

ADHD is Neurodivergence

To effectively address ADHD-related behaviors, it is crucial to recognize that these behaviors are not the result of intentional misconduct. Instead, they are manifestations of the unique brain functioning and chemical processes that characterize ADHD. Children with ADHD often grapple with impulse control, hyperactivity, and inattention. These behaviors can manifest in various ways, and parents need to understand the underlying causes.

Hyperactivity and Its Manifestations

Hyperactivity is a core characteristic of ADHD, and children often display behaviors such as:

- Fidgeting and Restlessness: Children with ADHD frequently find it challenging to remain still. They may constantly fidget, squirm, or tap their hands or feet.

- Excessive Talking: Hyperactive children may have difficulty regulating their speech. They might talk excessively, interrupt others, or dominate conversations without realizing it.
- Easily Distracted: Maintaining focus and attention can significantly challenge children with ADHD. They are prone to getting distracted easily, particularly in tasks that require sustained concentration.

Impulse Control Issues and Their Impact

Impulse control is another aspect of ADHD that significantly influences behavior. Children with ADHD often struggle with controlling their impulses, leading to behaviors like:

- Impulsiveness: They may act on their desires or impulses without considering the consequences. This can result in decisions and actions that can be dangerous or challenging to manage.
- Difficulty Waiting Their Turn: Waiting patiently can be incredibly challenging for children with ADHD. This difficulty can lead to frustration and problems with taking turns or following a structured order of tasks.

Rejection Sensitive Dysphoria (RSD)

While not exclusively a behavior, rejection-sensitive dysphoria (RSD) is a significant aspect of ADHD that profoundly impacts a child's emotional well-being. RSD involves heightened emotional responses to perceived rejection or criticism. This emotional response can manifest in various ways:

- Aggression: Children with RSD may respond aggressively when criticized or rejected. This aggression serves as a defense mechanism to shield themselves from emotional pain.
- Low Self-Esteem: Constantly experiencing heightened emotional responses to rejection can erode a child's self-esteem and lead to a negative self-image.
- Mood Swings: RSD can result in abrupt mood swings, where a child's emotional state can quickly shift from extreme highs to lows.

Stimming and Emotional Dysregulation

Some children with ADHD may engage in stimming, which involves repetitive movements or sounds. Stimming serves as a form of self-stimulation and emotional self-regulation. Emotional dysregulation, on the other hand, refers to the difficulty children with ADHD face in managing and expressing their emotions appropriately.

Teach Self-Regulation Skills

To help children with ADHD manage their behaviors effectively, it is essential to focus on teaching them self-regulation skills. Self-regulation encompasses the ability to control impulses, manage emotions, and react to situations in a balanced manner. Parents can play a crucial play a crucial role in reaching these vital skills:

- Coping Mechanisms: Equipping children with healthy coping mechanisms helps them manage stress, frustration, and emotional dysregulation more effectively. These mechanisms include deep

breathing exercises, mindfulness practices, and
sensory tools.

- Structure and Routine: Establishing consistent
  routines and systems provides a sense of predictability
  and stability for children with ADHD. Clear
  schedules and expectations make it easier for them to
  navigate daily tasks and responsibilities.

Empathetic Communication

Engaging in open and empathetic communication with your
child is essential. Encourage them to express their feelings and
concerns while validating their emotions. You can better
understand their needs and challenges by fostering a safe and
supportive communication environment for your child.
Effective communication also helps in building trust and
strengthening your parent-child relationship.

Collaboration with Professionals

In cases where ADHD behaviors are particularly challenging
or complex, seeking collaboration with healthcare professionals,
such as psychologists or behavioral therapists, can provide
valuable insights and guidance. Early intervention and
professional support significantly contribute to helping
children cope with ADHD and its effects.

Understanding and addressing ADHD-related behaviors
requires a compassionate and informed approach. By
recognizing that this behavior reflects neurodivergent brain
functions, parents can better support their children. Teaching
self-regulation skills, providing structure, and fostering
empathetic communication are essential strategies to help
children with ADHD navigate the complexities of their
condition.

Fostering Coping Mechanisms in Children With ADHD

It is essential to explore effective management tips and coping mechanisms to help children with ADHD navigate their behaviors, including episodes of rage, stimming, and meltdowns. It's essential to approach these challenges with patience, understanding, and strategies tailored to your child's specific needs.

One of the fundamental principles of managing ADHD-related behaviors is ensuring that your child's basic needs are consistently met. When a child's physiological and emotional needs are fulfilled, they are better equipped to manage their behaviors effectively. Here are some key aspects to consider:

- Healthy Diet: Proper nutrition plays a significant role in managing ADHD symptoms. A balanced diet rich in nutrients can help stabilize mood and improve attention and focus.
- Adequate Sleep: Ensuring your child gets enough restorative sleep is crucial. Sleep deprivation can exacerbate ADHD symptoms, leading to increased irritability and impulsivity.
- Regular Physical Activity: Encouraging your child to engage in regular physical activity can help them release pent-up energy and improve overall well-being.

The SAIL Strategy—A Coping Tool: The SAIL strategy is a helpful tool for children with ADHD to navigate situations and manage their emotional responses effectively. SAIL stands for:

- Stop: Teach your child to pause when they feel overwhelmed or frustrated. Taking a moment to stop and breathe can prevent impulsive reactions.
- Assess: Encourage your child to assess the situation calmly. Help them identify their feelings and thoughts, allowing for a more thoughtful response.
- Isolate: Suggest isolating the core issue or problem. This step helps your child focus on the root cause of their distress.
- Liberate: Guide your child in finding a solution or coping mechanism to address the issue. Emphasize the importance of problem-solving and seeking help when needed.

Praise and Reward: Positive reinforcement is a powerful tool in promoting desired behaviors in children with ADHD. Offering recognition and rewards when your child follows the rules and exhibits positive behavior can be highly effective. It's essential to:

- Provide Clear and Effective Feedback: Offer specific praise and feedback when your child displays positive behaviors. Reinforce empathy and forgiveness, even when they challenge you. This approach helps boost their self-esteem and encourages the development of empathy.
- Consistency Is Key: Ensure that you consistently acknowledge and reward positive behaviors. Consistency reinforces the connection between good behavior and positive outcomes.

Anti-Rage Technology: Exploring anti-rage technology may benefit children who experience rage episodes. Anti-rage technology includes apps and devices to help individuals manage and control their anger and emotional outbursts. These tools can provide valuable support in moments of crisis.

Staying Active: Physical activity offers an excellent outlet for children with ADHD to channel their excess energy and manage their behaviors. Activities such as sports, dancing, or regular playtime can help release built-up tension and improve focus.

Limiting Distractions: Children with ADHD are often highly sensitive to distractions, making it challenging to concentrate on tasks. Creating a focused environment is essential:

- Minimize Visual Distractions: Remove unnecessary clutter and distractions from your child's workspace or play area.
- Use Noise-Canceling Headphones: These can be particularly helpful when studying or doing homework.
- Establish a Consistent Routine: Consistency and structure provide a predictable environment to help children with ADHD stay on track.

Frequent Breaks and Unstructured Time: Children with ADHD may benefit from frequent breaks and unstructured time to decompress. These breaks allow them to recharge and prevent burnout. Incorporating short, unstructured periods into their routine can be highly effective.

Avoid Overloading: Tailoring your expectations to your child's capabilities and limitations is essential. Avoid overloading them with tasks or activities, especially during high-stress periods. Recognize that a child with ADHD may struggle more in the mornings or when transitioning between tasks.

Thought Journals: For children who find it challenging to express their thoughts and feelings verbally, thought journals can provide a private outlet. These journals allow children to write down their thoughts, questions, and concerns, helping them share their inner world positively and more structured.

Mindful Activities: Teaching children with ADHD mindful activities can aid emotional regulation. These activities encourage self-awareness and help children manage their emotional responses more effectively. Simple mindfulness exercises, such as deep breathing or guided imagery, can be introduced to their daily routine.

Creating a Boredom Box: A boredom box is a container filled with various activities and items children can engage with independently when bored or restless. Encouraging your child to use the boredom box fosters independence and provides an alternative to stimming or other less desirable behaviors.

Martial Arts and Structured Activities: Structured activities like martial arts can benefit children with ADHD. These activities teach self-control, discipline, and self-awareness. Additionally, they offer an outlet for physical activity, which can help manage hyperactivity and impulsivity.

Managing behaviors in children with ADHD requires a multifaceted approach, considering each child's unique needs and challenges. By addressing basic needs, implementing coping strategies, and providing support and structure, parents can empower their children to develop positive behaviors and effectively navigate the complexities of ADHD. Remember that every child is different, and it may take time to find the best strategies for your child. Patience, understanding, and ongoing communication are vital to helping your child thrive.

Understanding the Power of Reinforcement

Reinforcement is a fundamental concept in behavior management, and it plays a crucial role in helping children with ADHD modify their behavior. At its core, reinforcement involves using positive consequences to strengthen and encourage desirable behaviors while gradually reducing unwanted ones. Research has consistently shown that reinforcement strategies can improve attention and behavior in children with ADHD. Parents should understand and implement the following principles to effectively utilize reinforcement strategies.

Principle 1: Pay Positive Attention: One of the foundational reinforcement elements is providing positive attention to your child. Children with ADHD often exhibit boundless energy and a strong desire to communicate constantly. While this can sometimes become exhausting, positive attention to their excellent behaviors is a valuable investment. When you acknowledge and praise their positive actions, you reinforce those behaviors and motivate them to continue in the same vein.

Principle 2: Give Effective Instructions and Set Clear Boundaries: Children with ADHD may struggle with following instructions and comprehending boundaries. Communicating clearly and simply when providing instructions or setting limits is essential. Utilizing straightforward language and ensuring your child understands the expectations can help them process and adhere to your directive more effectively.

Principle 3: Praise Your Child's Efforts: Recognizing and praising your child's efforts, even when they haven't achieved perfection, can be highly motivating. Children with ADHD may face unique challenges in their tasks, and acknowledging their hard work and progress reinforces their determination and encourages them to persevere. Encouraging your child to take breaks when needed and teaching them to recognize when they require a little extra time to recharge can be instrumental in managing ADHD and maintaining their well-being. It's a valuable skill to balance tasks with self-care throughout life.

Principle 4: Ignore Mild Misbehavior: For minor disruptive behaviors, employing this strategy can be a valuable learning experience for children with ADHD. For instance, if a child refuses to complete their homework, ignoring it will help them realize that receiving a lower grade is the only outcome. Or not picking up toys will result in broken toys. Allowing them to experience these natural consequences can help them connect their actions to the outcomes.

Principle 5: Use Timeouts When Necessary: Timeouts can be effective when other strategies have not yielded the desired results. However, it is crucial to ensure that timeouts are applied consistently and are not the only form of discipline in the reinforcement plan. When used correctly, timeouts allow children to calm down, reflect on their behavior, and learn from their actions. Timeouts allow both the child and the parent to cool down and reflect. During these moments, parents can also introduce valuable breathing techniques, teaching their child how to manage emotions effectively and fostering a holistic approach to self-regulation.

Principle 6: Collaborate with Teachers: Collaborating with your child's teachers is paramount to maintaining consistency in behavior management strategies between home and school environments. Open communication allows the teachers to implement similar reinforcement techniques, ensuring a unified approach to addressing your child's behaviors.

Principle 7: Establish a Reward System: Creating a reward system can be a powerful motivator for children with ADHD. A well-designed behavior/reward chart can help track progress and provide positive reinforcement for desirable behaviors.

Designing a Behavior/Reward Chart:

- Develop a chart with specific behaviors or tasks to focus on.
- Utilize colorful stickers, stars, or tokens to mark each completed behavior.
- Set achievable goals and rewards that are meaningful to your child.
- Maintain consistency in tracking and rewarding behaviors.

Ideas for Rewards:

- Extra Playtime
- Choosing a Favorite Movie or Activity
- Small Treats or Snacks
- Special Outings or Adventures
- Praise and Positive Attention

In conclusion, reinforcement strategies and positive discipline techniques can be powerful tools for parents of children with ADHD. These strategies not only promote positive behavior choices but also help in reducing unmanageable ones. By consistently implementing these principles and collaborating with teachers and caregivers, parents can create a supportive environment where their children can thrive. The interactive element of helping parents design a behavior and reward chart empowers parents to apply these techniques effectively in their daily routines.

As Roy L. Smith wisely noted, "We are apt to forget that children watch examples better than they listen to preaching." Therefore, parents must provide guidance and strive to be positive role models. Parents must prioritize their mental health and well-being, as reducing stress and maintaining a healthy dynamic can significantly impact a child's development. As we move forward, let's continue to explore the *BEATITUDE* solution and delve into the next step, designing a new family dynamic that nurtures the growth and well-being of every family member, including those with ADHD.

Chapter 8
Design a New Family Dynamic Where Everyone Thrives

Parenting a neurodivergent child with ADHD often requires more than individualized support. It necessitates an effective approach that considers the entire family's well-being. Let's examine the importance of creating a harmonious family dynamic and explore various strategies and fun ideas. It's crucial to approach this transformation with kindness, compassion, and gentleness, considering every family member's mental health, awareness, and quality of life could be at risk.

Siblings of children with ADHD can and often experience higher stress than their peers in non-ADHD families. Research has even shown that the child with ADHD and their siblings share similar perceptions of their own or each other's quality of life. This emphasizes the urgent need for parents to proactively work on positively shaping family interactions. By doing so, not only can they improve the mental health of the child with ADHD but also enhance the well-being of their partner, other children, and everyone residing in their home. This chapter explores strategies to help you achieve this transformation and create a nurturing environment where everyone can thrive.

Understanding ADHD's Impact on the Family

ADHD doesn't merely affect the diagnosed child; its repercussions ripple throughout the entire family structure. It's essential to acknowledge these far-reaching effects to initiate the process of creating a more harmonious family dynamic. Siblings, often overlooked in this context, bear a considerable emotional burden. Research suggests they often experience elevated stress levels and less enjoyable experiences than other children. Additionally, a child with ADHD faces unique challenges in navigating familial relationships (Pryor, 2021). Therefore, recognizing the multifaceted impact of ADHD on the family is the first step in incorporating positive change.

Addressing Reluctance Within the Family

One of the initial challenges parents face is often dealing with reluctance from other family members. These individuals might not fully comprehend the complexities of ADHD, leading to misunderstandings, embarrassment, guilt, shame, or emotional dysregulation. In such instances, education is a powerful tool for bridging gaps and building understanding.

Educating the family involves sharing comprehensive information about ADHD, including its causes, its impact on daily life, and the strategies available to manage its challenges effectively. Family therapy or counseling can also prove invaluable, providing a safe platform for family members to express their concerns, seek answers to their questions, and work collaboratively to enhance communication and relationships. By involving every family member in the learning process, parents can establish a support network that is well-informed and empathetic, laying the foundation for a more compassionate and understanding family unit.

Managing Behavioral Disruptions and Conflict

Behavioral disruptions and conflict often become part of the daily narrative within families contending with ADHD. Brothers or sisters may become frustrated by their neurodiverse sibling's behavior, creating tensions among family members. To manage these situations effectively, parents can employ various strategies.

One essential approach is to defuse conflicts and address behavioral disruptions promptly. This involves maintaining composure despite challenging behaviors, utilizing positive discipline techniques to handle issues, and ensuring consistency in enforcing rules and consequences. A helpful tactic is to let each child take time in their own space to calm their emotions and rationally think about the argument. Parents can also teach conflict resolution skills to all family members, empowering them to express their feelings and resolve disagreements constructively.

Promoting Self-Awareness and Mindfulness as a Family

Self-awareness and mindfulness within the family unit can contribute to cultivating a more harmonious dynamic. Children with ADHD can benefit from learning techniques to manage their symptoms and emotions, while other family members can gain a deeper understanding of their reactions and responses.

One way to achieve this is by engaging in mindfulness practices as a family. Activities such as deep-breathing exercises, meditation, or yoga can help family members become more attuned to their emotions and reactions, encouraging self-regulation and empathy. Furthermore, parents can discuss emotions openly, providing each family member with a safe space to express their feelings and concerns without fear of judgment.

Avoiding Unproductive Family Roles

Within families dealing with ADHD, unproductive roles can manifest among family members. These roles include allying, scapegoating, defensiveness, excuse-making, and enabling. Identifying and addressing these roles is vital for creating healthy family relationships.

For example, scapegoating occurs when one family member becomes the target of blame or frustration for the child's ADHD-related challenges. This can exacerbate tension within the family. Parents should actively discourage scapegoating and promote a collaborative approach to problem-solving instead. By focusing on solutions rather than assigning blame, families can work together to support the child with ADHD and each other.

Enabling, conversely, involves unintentionally allowing the child with ADHD to evade responsibility or consequences for their actions. Parents can prevent enabling by setting clear expectations and boundaries, consistently enforcing rules, and holding all children accountable for their behavior. Addressing reluctance within the family can manifest in various ways, including siblings who might blame the child with ADHD for household issues or tease them due to misunderstandings. Creating an open, empathetic environment that addresses these dynamics and encourages healthy sibling relationships is essential. Additionally, involving your children in developing these rules and consequences can foster a sense of ownership and responsibility.

Understanding the far-reaching impact of ADHD, addressing reluctance through education and involvement, managing behavioral disruptions, promoting self-awareness and mindfulness, and avoiding unproductive family roles are key steps in this transformative process. Parents can create a nurturing and supportive environment where everyone thrives by taking a proactive and compassionate approach.

Designing a New Family Dynamic

Parenting a child with ADHD requires reshaping the family dynamic to ensure every member feels valued, appreciated, and loved. Balancing attention, promoting open communication, collaborating with your partner, and fostering a sense of belonging with the family are essential aspects of creating a nurturing environment. This leads us to explore strategies to achieve these goals, ultimately strengthening family bonds and facilitating growth and happiness for everyone involved.

Balancing Attention Within the Family

One of the fundamental elements in designing a new family dynamic is striking a balance when it comes to attention and support for each family member. ADHD can often consume a significant portion of parental engagement due to the unique needs of the child with ADHD. However, it's crucial not to overlook the needs and desires of other family members, including other children and your partner.

A key strategy is to dedicate one-on-one time with each family member, ensuring everyone feels heard and valued. Spend quality time alone with your partner, other children, or even extended family members living in the household. This individualized attention strengthens your connections and conveys the message that every member is essential. It's a way of nurturing healthy relationships and preventing feelings of neglect or resentment.

Empowering Every Voice in the Family

Communication is pivotal in providing understanding, empathy, and cooperation in a family. To create a space where everyone feels appreciated, allowing every member to have a voice is crucial. This includes not only parents and the child with ADHD but also siblings and other relatives.

Implementing regular family meetings can provide a platform for open communication. Encourage family members to share their thoughts, feelings, and concerns. These meetings can be an opportunity to brainstorm solutions to challenges or conflicts. By involving everyone in decision-making, you promote inclusion and encourage teamwork and contentment within the family.

Collaborating With Your Partner

Your partner is a critical ally in your journey to design a new family dynamic. Effective co-parenting and collaboration with your spouse or partner are vital to creating a nurturing environment. Maintaining a united front and sharing the responsibilities of parenting can significantly reduce stress within the family.

Confer with your partner regularly to discuss your child's progress, any challenges that have arisen, and strategies that are working well. When both parents are on the same page, it provides stability and consistency for the child with ADHD and a harmonious atmosphere for the entire family.

Establishing Clear Roles and Responsibilities

Family roles and responsibilities can provide structure in the daily life of an ADHD child, leading to fewer family issues. It is essential for everyone to understand their roles and responsibilities to enable a sense of belonging and inclusion. This clarity helps in reducing misunderstandings and conflicts.

Create routines and schedules that allocate tasks and responsibilities to each family member. These can include chores, school-related duties, and recreational activities. Having well-defined roles ensures everyone knows what is expected of them and what they can expect from others. It contributes to a smoother daily routine and reduces stress for the child with ADHD and other family members.

Simplifying Transitions and Embracing Technology

Children with ADHD often struggle with transitions, finding them overwhelming or anxiety-inducing. It's crucial to have straightforward measures to prevent anyone in the family from becoming stressed or agitated during these times. Prepare your child and the family for transition by providing clear and precise instructions. Use visual aids or timers to help your child understand when a change will occur and what to expect. Consistency in these strategies can ease the process and minimize disruptions within the family.

Technology can also play a helpful role in managing family life. Utilize digital tools, apps, or calendars to organize schedules, set reminders, and share responsibility. Technology can particularly benefit children with ADHD, who may respond well to visual cues and structured routines.

Addressing ADHD Within the Entire Family

ADHD can be hereditary, and it's possible that other family members, including yourself, your partner, or even other children, may also have ADHD. Recognizing and addressing ADHD within the entire family is essential for creating an environment where everyone feels understood and supported.

Seek professional evaluation and support if such concerns arise. Understanding your neurodiversity can lead to increased empathy and effective communication within the family. Additionally, it can help you develop strategies that cater to the specific needs of those family members with ADHD.

Creating Meaningful Family Rituals

Consider implementing meaningful family rituals to create a sense of togetherness and strengthen family bonds. These activities range from simple daily routines to unique traditions everyone can appreciate. Activities such as cooking together, family game nights, or movie nights provide opportunities for bonding and shared experiences. Choose games that challenge your ADHD child's memory or problem-solving skills to make them feel engaged and accomplished. Meaningful interactions, such as storytelling or sharing personal experiences, can also deepen family connections and allow everyone to get to know each other better.

Balancing Your ADHD Child's Needs

While it's essential to cater to your child's unique needs with ADHD, it's equally crucial to maintain a balanced family dynamic that considers the well-being of everyone. In this section, we will explore strategies and techniques to address sibling conflicts, orchestrate bonding time, establish routines, create outlets for all family members, celebrate individual strengths, and ensure a moment of respite within the family.

- Addressing Sibling Conflict: Sibling conflicts can be a significant source of stress, unrest, or conflict within a family dealing with ADHD. It's common for siblings to feel overshadowed by the attention given to a child with ADHD, leading to resentment and tension. To address this issue, it's essential to recognize and validate the feelings of all your children. Allow them to express their emotions and concerns openly. Provide a platform for them to communicate their frustration and fears. Acknowledging their feelings can create an environment where they feel understood.

- Orchestrating Bonding Time: To strengthen the bonds among family members, including siblings, your ADHD child, and your partner, consider dedicating specific bonding time for each pair or group. Create opportunities for siblings to spend quality time together doing activities they enjoy. Plan outings or activities that cater to their interests. Likewise, carve out special moments for you and your ADHD child to connect. This individualized attention helps foster positive relationships and ensures that everyone feels valued.

- Codifying Family Routines: Routines play a pivotal role in creating stability within a family—Codify family routines to ensure everyone knows what to expect and when. Establishing family habits can help reduce anxiety and conflicts, especially for a child with ADHD who thrives on structure. Involve the entire family in the process of creating and following routines. This includes morning and bedtime routines, mealtime schedules, and designated homework or study hours. When everyone adheres to the same practices, it fosters a sense of unity and predictability within the family.

- Creating Outlets for Everyone: Every family member, whether they have ADHD or not, benefits from having outlets to express themselves and relieve stress. Encourage each family member to pursue their interests and passions outside the family dynamic. Support your children in discovering and engaging in hobbies or extracurricular activities they are passionate about. This provides them with a sense of accomplishment and allows them to develop their interests and skills.

- Celebrating Individual Strengths: In a family, it's essential to celebrate the unique strengths and talents of each child. It's vital to highlight and appreciate the positive qualities of your child with ADHD and their siblings. Acknowledge and praise each child's achievements, whether they are academic, creative, or related to other interests. This recognition nourishes self-esteem and reinforces that every family member has something valuable to contribute.

- Ensuring Time Apart: Everyone in the family must get their valued alone time where they can be to themselves. Taking care of a family is demanding, and taking breaks is essential for everyone's well-being. Plan and schedule regular "timeouts" when each parent can have some personal space and relaxation. Additionally, consider organizing playdates, sleepovers, or outings for your children to interact with friends or extended family outside the home. These breaks provide opportunities for rejuvenation and can help reduce stress within the family.

Balancing your ADHD child's needs with those of your partner and other children is essential for maintaining a harmonious family unit. By addressing sibling conflicts, orchestrating bonding time, codifying family routines, creating outlets, celebrating individual strengths, and ensuring moments of respite, you can create an environment where everyone feels valued, supported, and happy. Balancing these needs may require patience and effort, but your family's harmony and well-being are worth it.

Fun Ways to Bond With Your Partner

When parenting an ADHD child, the bond between you and your partner may lessen, and you can grow apart. Here are ten exciting ways to bond with your partner:

1. Explore a New Hobby Together: Embark on a journey of discovery by picking up a shared hobby or interest. Whether learning a new language, painting, or even taking dancing classes, exploring new activities together can be a great way to strengthen your connection.
2. Plan a Surprise Date Night: Surprise your partner with a thoughtfully planned date night. It could be a romantic dinner at their favorite restaurant, a cozy movie night under the stars, or an adventurous outing to a place you've both wanted to visit.
3. Take a Weekend Getaway: Escape from the daily routine by planning a weekend getaway. It could be a relaxing retreat at a spa resort, an adventurous

camping trip, or a cultural exploration in a nearby
city.

4. Cook a Special Meal as a Team: Collaborate in the
kitchen to prepare a special meal together.
Experiment with new recipes, share cooking
techniques and enjoy the delicious results of your
joint effort.

5. Engage in an Adrenaline-Pumping Activity: Get your
hearts racing by engaging in an exciting and
adrenaline-pumping activity. Whether it's skydiving,
bungee jumping, or even a thrilling amusement park
ride, these shared experiences can create lasting
memories.

6. Attend a Live Performance or Event: Immerse
yourself in the entertainment world by attending a
live performance or event. Whether it's a theater
show, a sports game, or a comedy club, these outings
can be fun and enriching.

7. Create a Bucket List and Start Ticking Items Off: Sit
down together and create a bucket list of experiences
you'd like to share. From traveling to specific
destinations to achieving personal goals, working on
this list can be a bonding experience. Try
incorporating both your dreams and ideas into a
shared bucket list.

8. Have a Movie Marathon at Home: Choose a theme or
a series of movies, stock up on popcorn and snacks,
and have a cozy movie marathon at home. It's a great
way to relax, unwind, and enjoy each other's
company.

9. Challenge Each Other to a Friendly
Competition: Engage in friendly competitions that
bring out your playful sides. Whether it's a board

game, a sports match, or a trivia quiz, these challenges can add a dose of excitement to your relationship. You can also incorporate these activities into family time.

10. Volunteer for a Charitable Cause as a Couple: Give back to your community and strengthen your bond by volunteering for a charitable cause. Whether participating in a local cleanup, helping a food bank, or supporting something you're passionate about, these shared experiences can be incredibly rewarding.

These ten activities offer a variety of ways for you to connect with your partner, create lasting memories, and keep the spark alive in your relationship. Whether you're seeking adventure, relaxation, or quality time together, there's something on this list for every couple to enjoy.

Maintaining a harmonious family life while balancing the needs of your ADHD child, partner, and other children is a challenging yet rewarding journey. Sibling conflicts can be a source of discord within families, but addressing these issues head-on can pave the way for better understanding and stronger bonds among your children.

Remember that your family is a team, and each member plays a vital role in its success. Through open communication, empathy, and shared experiences, your family can thrive, and each member can reach their full potential. In this journey, patience and dedication will be your allies, and the rewards of a harmonious family life are immeasurable.

Chapter 9
Explore What to Expect
to Prepare for the Future

As we begin the final leg of our *BEATITUDE* journey, we find ourselves at a crucial juncture in your child's life and your family's well-being. The path behind us has been filled with understanding, empathy, and actionable strategies to raise a neurodiverse child with ADHD successfully.

Studies confirm that a significant percentage of children with ADHD, between 35% and 78%, continue to carry the symptoms into adulthood (Wirth, 2023). This fact hits close to home, for I, too, experienced the challenges that arise when we fail to anticipate the transitions and evolutions that ADHD can bring. Yet, the *BEATITUDE* solution isn't just about managing the present; it's about embracing the changes that lie ahead and ensuring that you and your child can thrive together. We will examine what to expect as your child grows and matures and how to prepare for these changes in a way that ensures a happier and more harmonious family life.

Throughout this journey, we will remain supportive, motivational, and compassionate, drawing from expert insights and evidence-based approaches to help you and your child prepare for the future with confidence and optimism. In this chapter, we set our sights on the road ahead, armed with knowledge and a sense of purpose.

How ADHD Evolves With Aging

Understanding how ADHD evolves with age is essential for parents, caregivers, and educators to provide the most effective support to children with ADHD. While there are patterns in how ADHD symptoms change over time, it's crucial to remember that each person's experience is unique. Let's look into the most common issues that arise as children with ADHD grow, preparing you to discuss these changes with your family, support team, educators, and professionals.

First, it's essential to dispel two prevalent myths surrounding ADHD. The first myth is that ADHD worsens with age. Contrary to this belief, ADHD symptoms do not necessarily increase over time. However, it is equally important to understand that the second myth, which suggests that ADHD disappears with age, is also false. The answer lies somewhere in the middle, with each case distinctly different. ADHD persists in adulthood for many individuals, although the presentation and impact may change.

The type of ADHD your child experiences may also shift as they age. For instance, some children with predominantly hyperactive-impulsive symptoms may later exhibit more inattentive symptoms or vice versa. This change in symptom presentation can influence how an individual approaches and continuously manages ADHD.

One critical question parents often ask is, At what age do ADHD symptoms peak? Research suggests that the age of peak symptoms will vary from person to person (Cherney, 2022). It's essential to remember that receiving an ADHD diagnosis at a young age doesn't mean that symptoms will necessarily be at their most challenging during childhood. Some individuals may see peak symptoms during adolescence or even adulthood.

As your child grows, their ability to self-regulate may improve. In individuals without ADHD, self-regulation naturally develops over time, with infants having limited self-control and adults exhibiting greater self-regulation. Children with ADHD may initially lag behind their peers but can improve and thrive. While they may not match the self-regulation abilities of their neurotypical peers, success is possible.

However, it's important to note that children with ADHD may still face challenges as they age. Three specific areas may manifest in more pronounced ways due to differences in executive and neurological functions:

1. *Academic Challenges:* Managing academic demands can become increasingly difficult as children transition to more complex educational environments, such as middle school, high school, and college. Balancing coursework, assignments, and extracurricular activities can be particularly challenging.

2. *Hyperactive Symptoms:* Hyperactive symptoms, such as excessive running or climbing, talking excessively, or being constantly "on the go," often decline as children enter later childhood and early adolescence. These physical manifestations of hyperactivity can evolve into a sense of restlessness.

3. *Impulsivity:* Impulsive behaviors can improve with age, but the consequences of impulsive actions may

become more serious. Adolescents and adults with ADHD may face increased risks, such as impulsive spending or substance abuse, as they struggle with impulsive tendencies.

In contrast to these changes, inattentive symptoms remain the most stable as a person ages. While an individual's attention span may gradually improve with age, it might not reach levels sufficient to meet daily demands. As a result, inattentive symptoms often persist into adulthood.

Additional symptoms tend to remain consistent with age. These include difficulties with time management, organization, and initiating tasks, which can persist throughout an individual's life. Recognizing these constant challenges will guide you in implementing strategies to help your child manage them effectively.

Emotional regulation, while slow to develop, often improves as children with ADHD grow into adolescence and childhood. As individuals better understand emotional responses, they can develop strategies to manage their feelings and reactions more effectively.

However, it's essential to be aware that certain aspects, such as working memory and "brain fog," may deteriorate with age. Working memory refers to our inability to hold and manipulate information temporarily. Working memory can naturally decline as individuals age, which can be particularly challenging for those with ADHD. "Brain fog" is another symptom that may increase with age, impacting one's ability to think clearly and efficiently.

Tweens, Teenagers, and Young Adults

As children with ADHD transition into their tweens, teens, and early adulthood, they often carry specific challenges, such as motivation issues, disorganization, and increased restlessness. These struggles can impact their academic performance, relationships, and overall well-being. Therefore, parents and caregivers must provide guidance, techniques, and tools to help them navigate these challenges effectively. Let's explore a range of strategies and tips that can empower tweens and teens with ADHD to develop the skills needed to thrive:

- Help Stay Organized and Focused: Losing track of what's required for school or daily tasks can be expected for tweens, teens, and early adults with ADHD. Teaching them organizational techniques, such as creating to-do lists, using calendars, or creating a message board, can significantly improve their ability to stay on top of their responsibilities.
- Teach How to Break Overwhelming Tasks into Smaller Ones: Large or complex tasks can be daunting for individuals with ADHD. Teaching them how to separate tasks into basic, manageable steps will help them maintain focus and achieve a sense of accomplishment.
- Consistent Calm Communication: Communication is imperative when interacting with those with ADHD. Using calm, clear, and positive communication can create a supportive environment that fosters motivation and self-esteem.
- Provide Activities and Tools to Develop Self-Regulation Skills: Emotional regulation can be challenging. Equipping them with activities and tools, such as mindfulness exercises, a thought journal, or

stress-relief techniques, will help them learn to develop their self-regulation skills continually.

- Praising Good Behavior: Positive reinforcement remains essential for those with ADHD. Acknowledging and honoring good behavior, personal accomplishments, and ongoing successes can motivate them to prosper. It's vital to emphasize the value of praising them for positive actions and the ability to recognize their behaviors and actively work on self-improvement. Supporting their self-awareness and personal growth efforts is commendable and can further boost their motivation and self-esteem.
- Help Set Goals and Pursue Them: Goal-setting can be a powerful motivator. Encouraging individuals with ADHD to set achievable goals, academically or personally, and helping them create vision boards, dream boards, or action plans can keep them focused and driven.
- Encourage them to Remain Realistic: Setting realistic expectations is crucial to prevent demotivation, lack of focus, and frustration. Help them recognize their strengths and limitations, ensuring their expectations align with their abilities. For example, with new jobs or romantic relationships.
- Connect Uninteresting Ideas to Interesting Activities: To boost motivation, find ways to connect uninteresting tasks to activities or subjects they find engaging. You can enhance their focus and willingness to participate by making learning more enjoyable. They can incorporate what they learn into their teenage and adult years.
- Encourage Organization Skills: Organizational skills are vital for tweens, teenagers, and young adults with

ADHD. Start teaching the organizational techniques from a young age. For instance, color-coding items, establishing routines, and providing tools like sticky notes and daily planners can help. Utilizing lists is a valuable tool for managing everyday tasks and keeping track of essential things to remember. Lists can help individuals, especially those with ADHD, stay organized, prioritize tasks, and ensure nothing important is overlooked.

By implementing these strategies and maintaining open communication, you can support your child as they mature and help them overcome the challenges associated with ADHD. Remember to reassure them that you will continue to provide guidance and support as they grow, emphasizing your unwavering commitment to their future success. Remembering that ADHD is a lifelong journey, and the support and understanding should continue into adulthood. Whether your child is in grade school or an adult starting a career, being there to help manage ADHD challenges together remains crucial to their success and overall well-being.

Empowering Your Child's Growth Through Interactive Activities

As parents, your journey through this comprehensive guide to understanding and supporting children with ADHD has equipped you with invaluable insights and strategies. You've gained a deeper understanding of ADHD's impact on your child's life, learned how to foster healthy communication, discovered methods for managing behavior and emotions, and explored ways to create a thriving family dynamic. Now, we dive into activities, tools, and games that can further enhance your child's skills and ensure they thrive in the future.

Daily Reading Habits: Reading is a gateway to knowledge and imagination. Motivate your child to develop a daily reading habit. Follow these steps or create your own:

- Create a cozy reading nook with comfortable seating and good lighting.
- Let them choose books that align with their interests.
- Set aside time each day for reading.
- Consider using online platforms like Epic, which offers a vast library of digital books to keep kids engaged.

Music Lessons: Music has the power to inspire and captivate. Encourage their interest in music with the following steps:

- Identify their musical preferences and interests.
- Enroll them in music lessons or classes tailored to their chosen instrument or style.
- Create a dedicated practice space equipped with the necessary instruments or equipment.
- Support their learning journey by attending their performance or practice sessions.

The Engage Project: The Engage Project incorporates motivational games and activities into your child's routine. Such as learning games, puzzles, and chess. Here's a way to get started:

- Explore motivational games suitable for their age and interests, such as video games that reward achievements.
- Set clear goals and rewards to incentivize their engagement.
- Ensure that screen time remains balanced with other activities and responsibilities.

Race to a Goal: Racing toward a goal can be an exciting way to boost motivation. Implement this activity with steps like these:

- Choose a goal, such as completing a project, improving a skill, or achieving academic success.
- Break the goal into smaller, manageable milestones.
- Create a visual representation of their progress, such as a chart or poster.
- Establish rewards for reaching each milestone to maintain motivation.

Visualization: Visualization exercises can sharpen focus and attention. Here's how you can incorporate this technique:

- Guide your child through visualization exercises, like picturing a serene beach, a waterfall, or a favorite place.
- Encourage them to describe what they see in their mind's eye and engage their senses.
- Practice visualization regularly to build their concentration skills. It can also increase their ability to manage emotions through visualization during stress or emotional challenges.

Story-Based Games: Story-based games combine focus and interest, making learning enjoyable. Here's how to engage your child:

- Choose interactive story-based games that align with their educational goals and interests.
- Play these games together, discussing the storylines and problem-solving challenges. You can even act out the stories.
- Celebrate their achievements and progress, fostering a sense of accomplishment.

Incorporating these interactive activities, tools, and games into your child's daily life can provide them with essential skills that serve them well as they grow. These activities address motivation and focus on their interests and passions, making learning an engaging and enjoyable experience.

In closing, let us remember the words of Edwin L. Cole, "There are dreamers, and there are planners, the planners make their dreams come true." During this journey, you have transitioned from a dreamer into a proactive planner with the knowledge, strategies, and tools needed to effectively support your child's growth and development. With planning, adaptation, and determination, you can continue to nurture your child's potential and create a brighter future for your family.

Conclusion

As our journey ends, it's important to reflect on the remarkable progress you have made in understanding and supporting your family and your child with ADHD. This has been a resource, a companion, and a guide through the intricate landscape of ADHD, offering insights, strategies, and hope to parents and families facing the challenges accompanying this neurodiverse condition. Here are some key takeaways from what you have learned:

- ADHD is a neurodevelopmental condition that can present unique challenges, but it also brings a wealth of creativity, energy, and enthusiasm to those who embrace it.
- Effective communication is the cornerstone of building strong relationships with your child and meeting their needs.
- Strategies for managing behavior and emotions, creating a harmonious family dynamic, and fostering skills for the future are essential tools in your ADHD tool kit.

First, we looked at understanding ADHD. We embarked on our journey by exploring the fundamentals of ADHD, dispelling myths, and gaining insight into the condition's intricacies. We then looked at communication and connections. Exploring how effective communication emerges as the cornerstone of building strong relationships, ensuring their needs are met while cultivating understanding and trust. Managing behavior and emotions guided us with practical strategies for helping children navigate their often intense and complex emotions.

Then, we looked at creating harmony in the family dynamic by encouraging a peaceful and thriving environment. We dove into nurturing mental health and managing stress and anxiety. We also found essential tips for managing education and advocating for our ADHD child's education. Finally, preparation for the future guided us to have set strategies and plans for a child with ADHD who is bound to grow up.

There are success stories that serve as beacons of hope for all parents navigating the world of ADHD. Think of well-known figures like Sir Richard Branson, Adam Levine, or Simone Biles —individuals who have succeeded and excelled in their respective fields despite facing the challenges of ADHD. Their stories remind us that ADHD is not a barrier to achievement; it's a unique lens through which the world can be viewed with creativity, innovation, and determination.

Now, we shift our focus to the personal success of my own child, who has thrived among peers, siblings, and family. The journey was transformative; he is now a 21-year-old man with an ambition to help the world. He constantly strives to continue understanding and improving his mental health while finding ways to be a resource to others. Through dedication, learning, and the unwavering love of a family united in their mission to support their child, he has found the path to joy and prosperity.

ADHD is just another word for fun, exciting and adventurous.

– Julie Posey

The journey ahead may not always be straightforward, but armed with knowledge and equipped with strategies, you have the mental tools to navigate the challenges when they arise successfully. Remember, seeking support from others is a vital part of this journey, one that benefits you and everyone.

I invite you to leave feedback or share your thoughts on how this book has helped you. Your experiences and insights can be valuable resources for others walking a similar road.

Remember that your journey with ADHD is a chapter in your life, but it is not the whole story. With unwavering support, love, and the tools you've acquired, you are laying the foundation for a future filled with happiness and success.

Glossary

1. 504 Plan: A plan developed to ensure that a child identified with a disability receives accommodations in the public-school setting.
2. Behavioral Therapy or Cognitive Behavioral Therapy (BT/CBT): A therapy focused on understanding and changing negative behaviors and/or thought patterns.
3. Comorbid: Refers to having two or more conditions or disorders simultaneously, e.g., ADHD and anxiety.
4. Executive Functions: Mental skills include working memory, flexible thinking, and self-control. That helps manage time, pay attention, change focus, regulate emotions, and multitask.
5. Hyper-focus: When a person with ADHD becomes deeply engrossed in something, often to the exclusion of anything else.
6. Individualized Education Program (IEP): A plan in a school setting that details the support of a student with needs. Developed for students in the U.S. public schools who need special education.
7. Mindfulness: Focusing on the present moment, used to help with ADHD symptoms.

8. Neurodiversity/Neuro-divergent: A term that describes individuals whose neurological functions differ from the norm, often used to describe ADHD, autism, dyslexia, etc.

9. Neurotypical (NT): Describing someone whose brain functions within the "typical" range, i.e., not neurodivergent.

10. Reinforcement Strategies: Techniques that use rewards or consequences to encourage certain behaviors.

11. RSD Rejection Sensitive Dysphoria (RSD): RSD is a psychological condition characterized by extreme emotional sensitivity and emotional pain regarding feelings of rejection and criticism. Individuals with RSD experience severe emotional distress when perceiving they have been rejected or criticized by important people in their lives.

12. Sensory Processing: How the brain processes and responds to sensory stimuli, often challenging for neurodivergent individuals.

13. Stimming: Self-stimulatory behavior, usually involving repetitive movements or sounds.

14. Dysregulation: An inability to modulate emotional responses.

15. Stimulant/Non-stimulant: Refers to the types of medication options for ADHD.

About The Brand

 HopeHarbour Publications stands out as a premier brand, meticulously crafting literature that delves into mental health and holistic well-being. We guide readers through their emotional and mental terrains by interweaving authentic stories with factual insights. Collaborating with seasoned therapists and wellness experts, we ensure that our content enlightens and offers practical strategies.

At HopeHarbour, we delve into the complex layers of the human psyche, curating a rich assortment of mental health and wellness books that align with diverse experiences and paths to healing.

HopeHarbour Publications shines as a guiding light, gracefully making sense of mental wellness and guiding individuals on their profound, transformative emotional journeys.

References

8 mindfulness exercises that also reduce stress. (n.d.). Hawaii Pacific Health. https://www.hawaiipacifichealth.org/healthier-hawaii/live-healthy/8-mindfulness-exercises-that-also-reduce-stress/#:~:text=meditative%20walking%20

ADHD and school changes. (n.d.). Centers for Disease Control and Prevention. CDC ADHD

ADHD Changes in children as they grow and develop. (2018, May 31). Nationwide Children's; 700 Children's - A blog by pediatric experts. NationWideChildrens

ADHD Statistics: New ADD Facts and Research. (2006, October 6). *ADDitude.* https://www. additudemag.com/statistics-of-adhd/#:~:text=46.7%20percent%20of%20children%20with

ADHD support group for parents. (n.d.). ADDA - Attention Deficit Disorder Association. ADD

Amen, D., & Amen, T. (2019, October 24). *Free guide: what to eat (and avoid) for improved adhd symptoms.* ADDitude. https://www.additudemag.com/download/adhd-foods-to-improve-symptoms/

Attention-deficit/hyperactivity disorder (ADHD) in children - Diagnosis and treatment - Mayo Clinic. (n.d.). www.mayoclinic.org

Bailey, E. (2014, February 24). *9 Ways to teach empathy to children with ADHD.* HealthCentral. https://www.healthcentral.com/slideshow/9-ways-teach-empathy-children-adhd

Barkley, S. (2022, September 25). *20 Questions parents of kids with adhd should ask teachers.* Power of Positivity: Positive Thinking & Attitude. https://www.powerofpositivity.com/adhd-parents-ask-teachers-these-questions/

Boom, K. (2022, September 17). *45 Cute & interesting things to do as a couple to deepen your bond.* Mindbodygreen. https://www.mindbodygreen.com/articles/things-to-do-as-a-couple

Booth, S. (2023, May 15). *Is your child's behavior problem ADHD?* WebMD. https://www.webmd.com/add-adhd/child-behavior-and-adhd#:~:text=If%20your%20child

Build self-esteem in your child with ADHD. (2017, November 9). CHADD. Chadd

Burch, K. (2023, August 23). *What causes sensory overload in ADHD?* Verywell Health. VeryWellHealth

Can mindfulness exercises help me? (n.d.). Mayo Clinic. https://www.mayoclinic.org/healthy-lifestyle/consumer-health/in-depth/mindfulness-exercises/art-20046356#:~:text=pay%20attention.

CDC. (2020, September 23). *Behavior therapy for young children with ADHD | CDC.* Centers for Disease Control and Prevention. CDC

CDC. (2021, January 26). *What is ADHD?* Centers for Disease Control and Prevention. CDC

CDC. (2022, June 8). *Data and statistics about ADHD | CDC*. Centers for Disease Control and Prevention. CDC

Centre, A. (2021, February 22). *6 Ways to improve communication with kids with ADHD*. The ADHD Centre. https://www.adhdcentre.co.uk/6-ways-to-improve-communication-with-kids-with-adhd/

Cherney, K. (2022, July 7). *Does ADHD get worse with age? Your FAQs*. Healthline. https://www.healthline.com/health/adhd/can-adhd-get-worse-as-you-age#age-of-peak:~:text=at%20what%20age

Cherry, K. (2022a, April 26). *9 Fun activities for kids with ADHD*. Verywell Mind. https://www.verywellmind.com/fun-activities-for-kids-with-adhd-5235327#:~:text=cooking%20is%20a

Cherry, K. (2022b, June 23). *How to find an ADHD Support group*. Verywell Mind. https://www.verywellmind.com/how-to-find-an-adhd-support-group-5324827#:~:text=for%20parents

Cleveland Clinic. (2022a, June 2). *Neurodivergent: What it is, symptoms & types*. Cleveland Clinic. https://my.clevelandclinic.org/health/symptoms/23154-neurodivergent

Cleveland Clinic. (2022b, October 6). *ADHD Medications: How they work & side effects*. Cleveland Clinic. Cleveland Clinic

Contributors, W. E. (2022, September 27). *How ADHD can affect your family*. WebMD. WEDMD

Contributors, W. E. (2023, February 16). *ADHD alternative treatments*. WebMD. WEBMD

Davidson, J. (2017, June 13). *Healthfully*. https://healthfully.com/216890-list-of-motivational-games-for-kids.html

deBos, K., Willard, C., & Buck, E. (2023, September 1). *Mindfulness for ADHD kids: 10 easy meditation exercises*. Www.additudemag.com. https://www.additudemag.com/download/mindfulness-for-adhd-kids-10-easy-meditation-exercises/

Des Marais, S. (2022, July 7). *How does ADHD affect your child's self-esteem?* Psych Central. https://psychcentral.com/childhood-adhd/strategies-for-helping-kids-with-adhd-build-self-confidence

Doyle, A., & Sherrell, Z. (2019, April 30). *Best ADHD apps of 2020*. Healthline. https://www.healthline.com/health/adhd/top-iphone-android-apps

Dunbar, R. (2022, January 7). *It's not what you say, it's how you say it* Spsp.org. SPSP

Editors, Add. (2019, October 23). *The ultimate guide to ADHD medication*. ADDitude. https://www.additudemag.com/download/ultimate-guide-adhd-medications/

Edwards, M. C., Schulz, E. G., & Long, N. (1995). The role of the family in the assessment of attention deficit hyperactivity disorder. *Clinical Psychology Review, 15*(5), 375–394. https://doi.org/10.1016/0272-7358(95)00021-g

Effective ADHD focus exercises that improve attention and concentration. (2022, September 7). Special Strong. https://www.specialstrong.com/effective-adhd-focus-exercises-that-improve-attention-and-concentration/#:~:text=the%20coin%20game

References

Eidens, A. (2020, October 20). *7 Fun activities to motivate kids to learn at home.* Epic Blog. https://www.getepic.com/learn/7-fun-activities-to-motivate-kids-to-learn-at-home/#:~:text=promote%20reading%20from

Family dynamics and ADHD. (n.d.). Boys Town https://www.boystown.org/parenting/article/pages/family-dynamics-and-adhd.aspx#:~:text=enabling

Family Therapy. (n.d.). Bay area center for ADD/ADHD. https://www.bayareaadhd.com/family-therapy.html#:~:text=family%20therapy%20is%20one

Fargo, S. (2020, December 12). *How mindfulness builds resilience: what science says.* Mindfulness Exercises. https://mindfulnessexercises.com/how-mindfulness-builds-resilience-what-science-says/#:~:text=resiliency%20is%20our%20ability

Free guide to natural ADHD treatment options. (2017, January 27). ADDitude. https://www.additudemag.com/download/alternative-adhd-treatment-guide/

Give your best shot quotes (3 quotes). (n.d.). www.goodreads.com GoodReads QUOTES

Gnanavel, S., Sharma, P., Kaushal, P., & Hussain, S. (2019). Attention deficit hyperactivity disorder and comorbidity: A review of literature. *World Journal of Clinical Cases, 7*(17), 2420–2426. https://doi.org/10.12998/wjcc.v7.i17.2420

Goally. (2023, June 19). *Free printable adhd routine chart.* Goally Apps & Tablets for Kids. https://getgoally.com/blog/free-printable-adhd-routine-chart/#:~:text=try%20goally%20%f0%9f%91%89-

Greenblatt, J. M. (2022, April 4). *Bad behavior? no. your child's ADHD symptoms are to blame.* www.additudemag.com. https://www.additudemag.com/bad-behavior-adhd-symptoms/#:~:text=criticizing%20%e2%80%9cbad%20behavior

Hallowell, E. (2021, June 6). *12 Ways to build strong ADHD relationships in families.* www.additudemag.com. https://www.additudemag.com/12-ways-to-build-strong-add-families/#:~:text=8.%20target%20the

Harpin, V. A. (2005). The Effect of ADHD on the Life of an individual, Their family, and Community from Preschool to Adult Life. *Archives of disease in childhood, 90*(1), i2–i7. https://doi.org/10.1136/adc.2004.059006

How stress affects your health. (2022, October 31). Apa.org. https://www.apa.org/topics/stress/health#:~:text=natural%20reaction

How to build a consistent daily routine for a child w/ ADHD. (2022, September 9). www.additudemag.com. https://www.additudemag.com/slideshows/daily-routine-for-adhd-child/#:~:text=many%20children%c2%a0with

How to help motivate a child with ADHD - Crisis & Trauma Resource Institute. (2022, October 31). ctrinstitute.com. https://ctrinstitute.com/blog/how-to-help-motivate-a-child-with-adhd/#:~:text=losing%20what%e2%80%99s%20required

How to improve your ADHD child's self-esteem | Study.com. (2020). study.com. https://study.com/blog/how-to-improve-your-adhd-child-s-self-esteem.html#:~:text=as%20we%20mentioned

How to reduce stress through mindfulness. (n.d.). Rehabilitation Research and Training Center-

Healthy Aging & Physical Disability . Reduce Stress Through Mindfulness https://www. facebook.com/webmd (2019). *Slideshow: Celebrities with ADD/ADHD.*

How to explain ADHD to teachers. Understood. https://www.understood.org/en/articles/7-tips-for-talking-to-your-childs-teacher-about-adhd

Hughes, L. (2022, September 9). *10 ADHD symptoms that change as you get older (and why).* www.getinflow.io. https://www.getinflow.io/post/adhd-symptoms-changing-with-age#:~: text=usually%20get%20worse-

IEPs in School: purpose of an IEP and the IEP process. (2019, August 5). Understood. https://www.understood.org/en/articles/understanding-individualized-education-programs#how_to_get_an_iep

Jaksa, P. (2023, April 25). *Use this sample schedule with kids with ADHD / ADD.* www.additudemag.com. https://www.additudemag.com/sample-schedule-adhd-morning-after-school-bedtime/#:~:text=routines%20affect%20life

Kelly, K. (n.d.). *ADHD Alternative treatment.* www.understood.org. https://www.understood. org/en/articles/adhd-alternative-treatment-what-you-need-to-know

Key, A. P. (2023, May 15). *ADHD in children: managing moods and emotions.* webmd. https:// www.webmd.com/add-adhd/childhood-adhd/adhd-children-mood-swings#:~:text=need% 20to%20know.-

Li, P. (2022, October 21). *50 Inspiring parenting quotes that get you through hard times.* Parenting for Brain. Parenting For Brain

Lockitch, G. (2022, July 4). *059 Louise VN Liebenberg: how unresolved trauma affects our lives.* Ask Dr. Gill. https://www.askdrgill.com/2022/07/04/059-louise-vn-liebenberg-how-unresolved-trauma-affects-our-lives/

Logan, A. (2021, May 27). *5 tips to manage ADHD in children.* Mayo Clinic Health System. https://www.mayoclinichealthsystem.org/hometown-health/speaking-of-health/5-tips-to-manage-adhd-in-children#:~:text=1.%20give%20praise

Logsdon, A. (2022, April 11). *8 Basic components of a child's IEP.* Verywell Family. https://www.verywellfamily.com/essential-parts-of-an-individual-education-program-2162702#:~:text=every%20iep%20must

Low, K. (2022, April 19). *Why children with ADHD need structure and routines.* VerywellMInd. VeryWellMind

Low, K. (2023, March 28). *8 Simple school strategies for students with ADHD.* Verywell Mind. https://www.verywellmind.com/help-for-students-with-adhd-20538#:~:text=a%20child%20with%20adhd%20who

Mae, A. (2021, September 20). *ADHD sensory overload: Causes, treatment, and more.* www.medicalnewstoday.com. https://www.medicalnewstoday.com/articles/adhd-sensory-overload#sensory-overload:~:text=sensory%20overload%20occurs

Marais, S. D. (2014, January 2). *How does ADHD affect your child's self-esteem?* Psych Central. https://psychcentral.com/childhood-adhd/strategies-for-helping-kids-with-adhd-build-self-confidence#adhd-and-self-esteem:~:text=according%20to%20a

References

Marissa. (2022, May 3). *Family rituals: 100+ examples, tips, & guide to bring your family closer!* A to Zen Life. https://atozenlife.com/family-rituals/#:~:text=game%20nights

Matheis, L. (2022, February 28). *How to set up a daily routine for your child with ADHD.* www.joonapp.io. https://www.joonapp.io/post/how-to-set-up-a-daily-routine-for-your-child-with-adhd#:~:text=many%20of%20our

Matlen, T. (2021, July 19). *ADHD Sensory overload: SPD and ADHD in children.* www.additudemag.com. https://www.additudemag.com/adhd-sensory-overload-spd-and-adhd-in-children/#:~:text=what%20is%20sensory

McCarthy, L. F. (2022, March 30). *The weight of ADHD on your marriage.* Attitude. Marriage/Stress/Parenting Child with ADHD

Miller, C. (2016, February 18). *Behavioral treatments for kids with ADHD.* Child Mind Institute; Child Mind Institute. https://childmind.org/article/behavioral-treatments-kids-adhd/

Miller, G. (2016, May 17). *ADHD Parenting: 12 Tips to tackle common challenges.* Psych Central. https://psychcentral.com/childhood-adhd/parenting-kids-with-adhd-tips-to-tackle-common-challenges#10.-use-technology-to-your-advantage:~:text=10.%20use%20technology

Parents of children with ADHD. (2023). Meetup.com. https://www.meetup.com/topics/parents-of-children-with-adhd/

Patel, H., & Pharm, M. (2018, June 4). *The impact of ADHD on learning.* News-Medical.net. https://www.news-medical.net/health/the-impact-of-adhd-on-learning.aspx#:~:text=depending%20on%20the

Patterson, J. (2022, October 20). *ADHD family dynamics: dealing with difficult family members.* www.additudemag.com. https://www.additudemag.com/family-dynamics-adhd-difficult-relatives/#:~:text=educate%20the%20family

Pietrangelo, A. (2017, April 12). *What is stimming and how can it be managed?* Healthline. HealthLine

Planner, D. of a J. (2020, December 29). *Planning quotes - 12 amazing quotes about planning to live by.* Diary of a Journal Planner. Quotes to Live By

Pryor, O. (2021, December 3). *ADD/ADHD and sibling relationships.* Children's Medical. https://www.npcmc.com/2021/12/03/add-adhd-and-sibling-relationships/#:~:text=they%20may%20feel%20side%2dlined

Publishing, F. S. (2019, June 27). *10 Strategies for helping students with ADHD cope with frustration.* Free Spirit Publishing Blog. https://freespiritpublishingblog.com/2019/06/27/10-strategies-for-helping-students-with-adhd-cope-with-frustration/#:~:text=allow%20students%20frequent

Quotations, S. com. (n.d.). *Fighting for your children quotes, quotations & sayings 2023 - Page 8.* Search Quotes. Fighting For Your Children

RabinerA, D. (2017, September 2). *How children's ADHD symptoms affect parents' feelings & behavior* – ADD Resource Center. https://www.addrc.org/how-childrens-adhd-symptoms-affect-parents-feelings-behavior/#:~:text=Results%20from%20this

Rejection sensitive dysphoria (RSD): Symptoms & treatment. (2022, August 30). Cleveland Clinic. https://my.clevelandclinic.org/health/diseases/24099-rejection-sensitive-dysphoria-rsd

Rouse, M. H. (n.d.). *How can we help kids with self-regulation?* Child Mind Institute. https://childmind.org/article/can-help-kids-self-regulation/#:~:text=you%e2%80%99re%20a%20parent

Saline, S. (2021, July 7). *Sibling relationships and ADHD: How to mend family conflict.* Additude Mag

Schreiber, J. E., Possin, K. L., Girard, J. M., & Rey-Casserly, C. (2013). Executive Function in Children with Attention Deficit/Hyperactivity Disorder: The Nih Examiner Battery. *Journal of the International Neuropsychological Society, 20*(1), 41–51. https://doi.org/10.1017/s1355617713001100

Searight, H. R., Robertson, K., Smith, T., Perkins, S., & Searight, B. K. (2012). Complementary and Alternative Therapies for Pediatric Attention Deficit Hyperactivity Disorder: A Descriptive Review. *ISRN Psychiatry, 2012*(10.5402/2012/804127), 1–8. https://doi.org/10.5402/2012/804127

Sherrell, Z. (2021, July 21). *What are the benefits of ADHD?* Www.medicalnewstoday.com. https://www.medicalnewstoday.com/articles/adhd-benefits#summary:~:text=people%20living%20with

Smith, S. (2018, October 4). *5-4-3-2-1 Coping technique for anxiety.* www.urmc.rochester.edu. https://www.urmc.rochester.edu/behavioral-health-partners/bhp-blog/april-2018/5-4-3-2-1-coping-technique-for-anxiety.aspx#:~:text=%3a%20acknowledge%20five

Socialization and altruistic acts as stress relief. (2019, March 13). MentalHelp.net. https://www.mentalhelp.net/stress/socialization-and-altruistic-acts-as-stress-relief/#:~:text=As%20we%20mentioned

Some communication strategies for parents of kids with ADHD. (2019, November 21). The ADHD Centre. https://www.adhdcentre.co.uk/some-communication-strategies-for-parents-of-kids-with-adhd/

Sosnoski, K., & Smith, J. (2012, June 9). *Everyday mindfulness: 6 tips for mindful living.* Psych Central. https://psychcentral.com/health/everyday-mindfulness#meditation:~:text=taking%20time%20to%20sit

Sprich, S. E., Burbridge, J., Lerner, J. A., & Safren, S. A. (2015). Cognitive-Behavioral Therapy for ADHD in Adolescents: Clinical Considerations and a Case Series. *Cognitive and behavioral practice, 22*(2), 116–126. https://doi.org/10.1016/j.cbpra.2015.01.001

srcset />Caroline M. is the editorial director of the C. M. (2022, April 12). *When parent and child both have ADHD.* Child Mind Institute. https://childmind.org/article/help-for-parents-with-adhd/

Structure Quotes. (n.d.). Brainy Quote. https://www.brainyquote.com/topics/structure-quotes#:~:text=everyone%20has%20their,ed%20reed

References

Studies link ADHD and communication problems. (n.d.). www.brainbalancecenters.com. https://www.brainbalancecenters.com/blog/adhd-and-communication-problems#:~:text=research%20from%20the

Submission successful! 5 pillars to manage ADHD. (n.d.). ADDA - Attention Deficit Disorder Association. https://add.org/5-pillars-submission-successful/

Teaching better organization to kids with ADHD. (2022, March 30). www.additudemag.com. https://www.additudemag.com/15-ways-to-teach-better-organization-to-adhd-kids/#:~:text=color%2dcode%20academic

Team, A. E. (2022, December 20). *Inside the ADHD brain: structure, function, and chemistry.* ADDA - Attention Deficit Disorder Association. https://add.org/adhd-brain/#:~:text=scientists%20have%20found

Team, A. E. (2023, April 6). *ADHD & sensory overload: managing overstimulation.* ADDA - Attention Deficit Disorder Association. https://add.org/sensory-overload-adhd/#:~:text=for%20those%20with

The surprising statistics of ADHD in education | (2013). study.com. Suprising Statistics of ADHD

The Understood Team. (n.d.). *What is a 504 plan.* www.understood.org. https://www.understood.org/en/articles/what-is-a-504-plan

Tips for cooking up ADHD-friendly nutrition. (2022, April 9). www.additudemag.com. https://www.additudemag.com/download/adhd-friendly-diet-cooking-tips/

Understanding ADHD: information for parents. (2019, September 25). HealthyChildren.org. https://www.healthychildren.org/english/health-issues/conditions/adhd/pages/understanding-adhd.aspx#:~:text=not%20all%20children

Vann, M. R. (2016, February 17). *After-school activities for children with ADHD - Child ADHD resource center.* EverydayHealth.com. https://www.everydayhealth.com/hs/adhd-children/afterschool-activities-for-children-with-adhd/#:~:text=art%20or%20music

Velkoff. (n.d.). *ADD Symptoms in boys vs. girls – what are the differences?* | *Drake Institute.* www.drakeinstitute.com. https://www.drakeinstitute.com/add-in-boys-vs-girls\

WA, A.-D. (2018). Speech and Language Disorders in ADHD. *Abnormal and behavioural psychology, 04*(01). https://doi.org/10.4172/2472-0496.1000134

WebMD. https://www.webmd.com/add-adhd/ss/slideshow-celebrities-add-adhd https://www.understood.org/en/people/72f4882b3d364f64b32cacbc9aa051ba (2019, October 1).

What is the difference between an IEP and a 504 Plan? | *AccessComputing.* (n.d.). www.washington.edu. https://www.washington.edu/accesscomputing/what-difference-between-iep-and-504-plan#:~:text=504%20plan%20defined

Wirth, J. (2023, June 6). *ADHD Statistics and facts in 2023.* Forbes Health. Forbes

Working with teachers to help your ADHD child be comfortable at school | *Study.com.* (2020). Study Dot Com

Printed in Great Britain
by Amazon

42623078R00096